PARALLEL

A Climate Revolution Plan

by

Ron Koss

Dedication

To the many millions across the globe who are resilient in their hope and determination to meet the global warming crisis.

To the many who will answer the call and come together to form a movement, a mighty bucket brigade of small and large actions that add up to a transformation of how we live and consume on our Earth.

To the "impossible" which may be a door to new horizons and not just a ceiling that declares the limitations of our human potential.

AND

To the many millions who will be displaced, the many who will die, suffer, and live lives without the stability and security of the Earth's planetary life support systems.

To the species that will become extinct because of climate change.

And to all the future prayers, tears, and trauma needlessly spoken, shed, and felt.... if.... we humans choose to react to tragedy rather than act to prevent it.

***

Contents

Preface

<u>Magical Thinking</u>

The climate revolution paradigm that follows below will be described by some as "Magical Thinking." This diminishment is both exasperating and yet to be expected. Exasperating because our present lives are surrounded by the magic of – once upon a time - Magical Thinking.

Cross the North American continent in 5 hours – Magical Thinking to everyone living in the 18th century.

Hold something in your hand and talk to someone else 10,000 miles away – More Magical Thinking.

Peace on Earth – Magical Thinking?

What is possible and what is not? What is real and what is not in the realm of our senses and understanding?

The fact is humankind does not have a uniform and conforming realm of senses, perceptions, and conceptions.

We can imagine what is possible. We can judge what is possible. But we don't know.

Countless times, the impossible has been proven to be possible. Countless times, so-called Magical Thinking was not delusional or fantastical, but rather a glimpse into the future.

So, what are our limits and what limits us?

How certain are you in your judgments?

And regardless, if the possible is failing us, what is the impossible that would not?

<u>Why this Book?</u>

I have not descended from Mount Olympus or Mount Sinai. I qualify as a notable nobody. Notable in that I can demonstrate a life of some accomplishment. A nobody in that, although I am capable of magical thinking or at least capable of being accused of it, I do not have a Magic Wand.

I am not sure if anyone mortal has one of those, but a magic wand

– small "m" small "w" – yes, those are in the hands of a relative few.

MacKenzie Scott, who recently gifted $2.7 billion to 286 high impact organizations, possesses such a magic wand. She alone, with her personal resources and her connections, could alter the subtitle of this little book from "A Climate Revolution Plan" to "A Climate Revolution Start-up – Applications being Accepted."

What follows in PARALLEL are big ideas in search of a village of magic wands. A money wand or wands and the hearts that generously gift money are, of course, needed. But money, to be of value, needs something of value to propel. In the pages that follow, there is something worthy of being propelled – a climate revolution plan of action that I have named PARALLEL, and that the world will soon know by the // logo.

PARALLEL is not the typical entrepreneurial idea seeking investors. It is not me seeking personal gain. It is not a crusade or a religion. It is a response to a recognition.

Earth is warming. This warming is accelerating. Life as we know it hangs in the balance. And these understandings are now common knowledge.

There is one more understanding.

Climate action, all of it, is falling short. We face a unique peril – the airplane that we are all riding on has its nose pointing steeply down and its landing gear is up. And we know it! Dire media reports filter down to us regularly. CO_2 concentrations are at record levels. The Amazon Rainforest is under attack. It is never good news. Some version of "Nose down, Landing gear up" is always the headline. Yet, we carry on as we are carrying on, without the urgency to sensibly fix the plane that no one should want to be on, but that no one can get off.

I recently listened to a podcast that General Electric has produced called *Cutting Carbon*. GE is one of the premier manufacturers of turbines that electrify the world. Their podcast effort is well-done and seems well-intended.

As I listened, I was struck by the following explanation that conventional thinking accepts as a matter of fact. One of the GE speakers stated that there are established technologies available to sequester carbon at a scale that might be consequential to combat rising CO_2 levels. But he went on to say that the "commercial drivers" are not in place to propel the use of these technologies to the prominence that is needed.

Is the world just a business? Some declare this as an immutable law. The "powers that be" who dictate our climate change story are obviously dedicated to making money. It does not appear to matter to them whether the plane we are all on crashes. There will still be money to be made after the crash, maybe even more than ever.

Who are the "powers that be?" Are they the amalgamated nature and impact of the stock market? Big oil and the like? Are they the push and pull of behemoth family wealth like that of the Koch brothers? Are they the dominating influence and pervasive effect of super-powers like the United States and China? Are the "powers that be" also immutable?

Even if the "world is a business" is a fixed point of reality, and I don't know that it is, the "powers that be" are not immutable. They are formidable, but their strength, in other words their clarity of purpose to make money, is also where the door to many possibilities lies. Money is money, whether it is made sequestering carbon or burning fossil fuels.

What if the perception of opportunity shifted? What if pulling the plane's nose up (de-carbonizing) and bringing the landing gear down (re-wilding) presented itself as the most compelling near, mid, and long-term money-making opportunities?

Impossible? At first glance, it is a big idea to swallow. A second glance shows favorable consumer trends and encouraging opinion polls. And the third glance? It's a piece of cake. Kidding.

"Favorable and Encouraging" are the reasons for my hope and the birth of *PARALLEL* in my imagination. It is not a utopian conception. Capitalism does not disappear. Rather, it is "we" who appear in force to catalyze into existence those commercial drivers that will, in turn, quicken the transformations necessary to meet the global warming challenge.

PARALLEL focuses on how to manifest this collective "we"..... and to do so now.

It is a big idea in need of a band of magic wand holding brothers and sisters. And that is who I hope some of you, the readers, will become. The leaders of *PARALLEL*; the warriors of *PARALLEL*; the healers; the bridge builders and the visionaries.

Also essential is the "most of us", the "we" who are unique and magical in our own right although not holding the kind of wands found in the hands of people like MacKenzie Scott, Bill McKibben or Al Gore, to name a few. I hope you, the most of us, will also somehow discover this little book and be ready to come together to become the next wave of "powers that be."

Still impossible? Yes, impossible for me, Ron Koss. This story chronicles, in part, my efforts and my failures to bring others to my climate activism thinking. But I do not believe that becoming "the powers that be" is impossible for "we," for us, together.

My journey to *PARALLEL* is intended to be a radio beacon from a parallel universe written in hopes that "we" will find each other.

Spring, Summer, Fall & Winter: 2019 – 2021

There are seasons to my // journey described in four parts. Part 1 starts in spring into summer 2019. My mind is fresh. Ideas are coursing through me like molten lava bubbling from deep within. My writing is dense. You may have to "dilute with water" to make it palatable. I feel inspired to flatten a steep learning curve. I am hopeful. I am anxious to share. And with my brother Arnie's support and presence, I find those people.

In Part 2, my pre-// ideas and impulses, many of them discovered in Part 1, meet the world for the first time, conveyed in a chronicle of 35 email outreaches and responses. I feel welcomed in these exchanges and yet also very much an outsider trying to get in. I am determined. I am in familiar territory as an entrepreneur. Kind of like riding a bike. I know what to do. I know what to expect.

The fall of 2019 approaches. The light dims and shortens and the shadows lengthen. I am not deterred. I am propelled forward by the light of the holidays and my growing discoveries and insights.

COVID-19 emerges in March 2020 and although it is spring again, it feels darker and more lifeless than any Vermont winter I can remember. I feel like my climate revolution impulse is also dying on the vine. As you read the cascade of emails from spring 2019 into summer 2020, you will witness in slow motion this death. It is painful.

Finally, the lights go out at the end of June 2020 with no more moves to make in a world paralyzed by the pandemic.

I accept defeat with little drama and slide into a summer-less summer where nowhere feels safe inside or out. Followed by a hugless winter of loneliness.

And then inexplicably, miraculously in March of 2021, a seed sprouts. Yes, new life emerges within me as the second COVID spring begins. It is a bright green shoot with a little sign attached that says - *PARALLEL* this Way.

But there is an irony to this fledgling rebirth. I have re-awakened to my writing in Part 3 of this story but am psychologically captive in a familiar haunt that I have come to call the "Valley of Death." If you stick with me through this journey, thick and thin, you also will get to know this place vicariously.

A conundrum then follows. How do I find a way to leave this grave valley, littered with the wreckage of so many broken dreams, modest and mighty, including my own?

Part 4 brings to me a "way to leave," a plan absent of grandiosity but capable enough to bring *PARALLEL* back into the light where a few tender branches have emerged as vaccinations bring our human community back together, where hugs have never felt so good, and where spring brings again the promise of possibility, even for something as seemingly impossible as the *PARALLEL* you will soon know.

Where do we go from here? Will we be more than the voices in our head? How do we meet the climate crisis?

Or do we?

PART 1
Spring into Summer 2019

Chapter 1 – The Lay of the Land

Twenty-three signatories, atop of the climate activist hierarchy, wrote in an April 3, 2019 open letter to the British *Guardian* newspaper the following: *"The world faces two existential crises, developing with terrifying speed: climate breakdown and ecological breakdown. Neither is being addressed with the urgency needed to prevent our life-support systems from spiraling into collapse."*

Bill McKibben, one of those signatories, wrote in his 2019 book FALTER.

> "We're the only creature who can decide not to do something we're capable of doing. That's our superpower..... So, yes, we can wreck the Earth as we've known it...as we're doing right now. But we can also not do that. We could instead put a solar panel on the top of every.... roof.....and if we do, then we will have started in a different direction.
>
> I do not know that we will make those choices. I rather suspect we won't – we are faltering now, and the human game has indeed begun to play itself out. That's what the relentless rise in temperature tells us.... But we could make those choices. We have the tools (nonviolence chief among them) to allow us to stand up to the powerful and the reckless, and we have the fundamental idea of human solidarity that we could take as our guide."

My question is what will drive us to the ethos that "we're all in it together," to that "human solidarity," to which Bill McKibben refers? What will organize the world in such a way that unleashes sufficient urgency to overcome cynicism, die-hard individualism, and undermining resignation?

How do we advance the ubiquity of solar panels and build a super-charged non-violent movement to re-wild and de-carbonize on behalf of everything we hold dear?

Is it fantastical to think that there are answers to the above questions obedient to the time constraints we seem to face?

This is where *FALTER* ends and where I want to begin.

I want to explore a paradigm shift that potentially leads us from faltering to enduring; that leads us away from individual silos of action and towards a unified climate and ecological movement.

I have named this new paradigm, *PARALLEL*. The pages that follow will explain why this name and will animate big ideas for a climate revolution for your consideration.

One Hopeful Request

As I lay out my thinking, try suspending disbelief for as long as you can. The "impossible" sometimes persists not because it truly is impossible but because we short-circuit our imaginations and insist that it is.

A Very Short History

Forty-five years ago, in 1976, after reading Rachel Carson's *Silent Spring* and feeling dis-empowered, a big idea jumped out at me – organic baby food. I saw baby food as the best way to grow the hodge-podge of small organic growers scattered across the country into a movement to counter pesticide spraying.

Eleven years later, in 1987, in Middlebury, Vermont, my twin brother Arnie and I launched the first organic baby food company in the U.S. – Earth's Best. This big, seemingly impossible idea at the time, has made and continues to make a difference, along with the many other organic foods companies that have followed over the years into the marketplace.

But to be clear, not enough of a difference.

The big ideas that follow were similarly envisioned after reading the dire April 2019 open letter in *The Guardian* and again feeling dis-empowered.

One penetrating question arose from this despair. It has fueled my efforts here.

If the possible is failing us, what is the impossible that would not?

Let's take this journey together on behalf of everything we hold near and dear on this miraculous planet. The plan below is a work-in-progress waiting for your ideas and inspirations to deepen it, sharpen it and even possibly re-direct it.

Become the Powerful

The sobering plea for "urgency" made by Bill McKibben, Naomi Klein, Greta Thunberg and the 20 other signatories in *The Guardian* speaks to the obvious – something essential is missing in our response to the climate crisis. The extraordinary efforts of yesterday and today are proving insufficient.

What is missing?

It is this. The ecological crisis is declared, but the action response, in total, is not a "crisis action" response. It is diffuse. It is piecemeal. It is not unified. The parts do not add up to a discernible whole.

Yes, there are plenty of organizations to join but there is no singular movement. There is no bucket brigade in motion galvanized in solidarity and connected to a unified intelligence kicking-butt.

Rather, there are thousands of independent "buckets," constantly looking for "water" and throwing as much of it as possible onto problem "fires" that become territories of action. This is not working sufficiently.

Indivisibility and unity of action is a known inspirational collective human response to crisis if all or many are thrown into it together. It is needed. It is still missing. It is possible.

I have imagined a *PARALLEL* economy coupled to this united climate revolution inspiration. Together, working hand in glove, their shared and singular purpose is to birth and buoy that metaphorical bucket brigade into action that re-wilds and de-carbonizes with the urgency needed to write an alternative ending to our human-made climate crisis story.

Bill McKibben writes in FALTER that "we have the tools to stand up to the powerful and reckless." *PARALLEL* sets out with the same objective and an additional one – to also become the powerful.

<u>The Only House in the Only Town is on Fire.</u>

Presently, there is too much of our human potential, in plain sight, sitting on the sidelines. The "building" is in flames, there are plenty of buckets and there is plenty of water. But too many people are watching or walking by thinking, "What can I do?" or "This isn't my problem." or "I'm too busy." or "The fire department will put it out." or "What fire, I don't see anything burning." And it's their house on fire!! The only house in the only town on the only planet!!

Grabbing a bucket seems futile to many. "What's my little bucket going to do?" "Corporations control everything." "What's my membership in Green Peace or NRDC or WWF or 350.org going to do?" And to others, the crisis remains an abstraction or is invisible. "I can still buy tuna fish. Gas is pretty cheap. There are seashells on the beach. The geese are migrating. Yesterday, it was -15F" ... and so on.

We need a short-cut to activate and direct the vast amount of untapped collective "potential." We need to find our way to that urgency. And if that way is not to just "stay the course," with activism strategies as they are and our economic paradigm as it is today, what is it then?

Game-Changer

The revolution starts with formalizing a conceptual agreement, made possible with a lot of creative and skilled collaborative input between scientists and activists, that I'm calling *Game-Changer*. In fact, it is already formed in spirit via many international environmental collaborations and loosely expressed within academia via consensus reports published by the Intergovernmental Panel on Climate Change (a UN body established in 1988).

The *Game-Changer* agreement not only represents an envisioned foundation for a global plan of climate action, it also delivers the nuts and bolts.

But *Game-Changer* is not the *Paris Climate Agreement*.

Paris has not succeeded in creating the urgency needed to preempt the writing of the dire open letter published in *The Guardian*. Certainly, it represents ground-breaking progress, but it has not coalesced as a unifying force of action capable of being independent of controlling influencers like national identity, power politics and big-business interests.

The *Paris Climate Agreement* captures a wish, an aspiration and even offers a road map, but has not proven to have the teeth and hence impact needed to be the gamer-changer we collectively need.

The wisdom of what we already know and the intention to abide by that wisdom are too often obscured and sidelined by forces and dynamics that persist in wielding ultimate power. These forces are much like dinosaurs doomed to extinction but still wreaking their havoc to the bitter end.

We need a momentous shift in who or what holds ultimate power. In my view, it must be wielded by a mobilized global populace with its angst and pent-up potential energy finally united and released in a movement of Climate Revolution activism coupled with Consumer Revolution activism. Efforts like the *Paris Climate Agreement* should serve as prologue for the next waves of transformative action.

Remember, if the possible is failing us, what is the impossible that would not? Answering this question is imperative. Most, if not all, ideas/impulses in response to the imposing challenge facing us will naturally seem far-fetched and unwieldy – impossible, in a word. However, in this situation "impossible" is not the end of the road, but rather a hopeful beginning.

Habituated thinking and the resistance that accompanies it are exactly what inertia depends on to keep things the same, no matter that the same, regarding our global climate, is akin to a determined lemming march to the cliff's edge and over.

The Heart

The heart of *Game-Changer* lays out an elaborate schematic of interconnected ecological flash points, ongoing actions, and key organizations and scientists involved – from global to local. It identifies and prioritizes an agreement for actions so that the "potential" human energy on our planet knows how to organize and where to go to become that virtual revolutionary bucket brigade.

To be clear, the aim is not to re-invent the wheel. Starting from scratch is not an option. An inclusive post-COVID series of symposiums across the globe uniting activists, environmental groups and scientists needs to be initiated or re-initiated. Collaborations, for example, with such climate mitigation efforts as *Project Drawdown* (founded in 2014 by Paul Hawken and Amanda Ravenhill) and the work of the Buckminster Fuller Institute are integral to formalizing *Game-Changer*. Coordination with 350.org, Natural Resources Defense Council, The Nature Conservancy, Environmental Defense Fund, Green Peace, the Sierra Club and others are a given.

Game-Changer, when ready, needs to be brought to the public in spectacular fashion – the biggest of debuts. The event needs to be a compelling, inspiring, and unifying call-to-arms, a BIG BANG moment of creative expression, clarity of purpose, possibility and know-how that must overcome inertia, cynicism, and dis-empowerment to galvanize the world with its ambition and focus.

The debut will showcase a compelling agreement – that both supports and builds upon the productive actions and initiatives that are already in motion and will provide a re-focused, re-prioritized and re-vitalized blueprint for the world community to meet the climate and ecological crisis with the needed urgency.

Most importantly, *Game-Changer* represents a united declaration of action. It will create the over-arching purpose for the next generation and the next: A Globe in Crisis – meets – A Globe in Action. Organizational silos do not disappear, but they are now in service to a greater whole and a unified effort.

What remains missing and essential is *Game-Changer's* complementary other-half, *PARALLEL.*

Game-Changer represents the brains or comprehensive global road map to meet the climate crisis. *PARALLEL* represents the know-how and means to be the economic brawn or power needed to drive that road.

Remember, standing up to the powerful and reckless is necessary but not sufficient to meet the climate crisis. Becoming the powerful, by creating a movement that is also an economic juggernaut, must happen.

But first, more on the– *Game-Changer* Road Map.

The Road Map

To fill this in a little more, re-wilding initiatives might be broken into 8 primary areas of activism (Forestlands, Grasslands, Mangroves, Salt Marshes, Peatlands, Deserts, Oceans, Seabeds). Each primary area is mapped out in elaborate depth. This map is "live." It is updated in real-time by thoughtfully configured designated oversight teams.

For example, mapping "Mangroves" means the identification of each key mangrove area across the globe; the status of each area; the organizations involved in each area; the projects in motion and/or planned; the key scientists and activists engaged; an assessment of the local communities affected; identifying the local leaders involved; results to date, problems, concerns, and recommended actions; and related critical paths.

For mangrove area by mangrove area, this work is meticulously done. The proposed mapping builds upon existing work and will be expanded upon and updated. Again, there is no reinventing the wheel intended. There are projects in Central Java and Suriname that are having success. There is the *Mangrove Action Project* that uses the *Community Based Ecological Mangrove Restoration* Approach that emphasizes local community participation.

There is much that has been learned and much learning to apply.

With the updated mapping complete, a "Summary for Mangroves" will be written, and a priority list created that directs, as part of the climate revolution, the "potential energy" in the form of humankind waiting to be a part of a "from-the-bottom-up" unified movement of action. Some of this potential will be expressed as money; some as local direct-action in affected areas; some as extensive outreach via media; some as research and monitoring; some as lobbying; and so on.

The Road Map details a projection of the expected outcomes for any given action as well as the related timeframe and how it will be measured and monitored. A chain of command is identified including oversight. Also, built-in redundancies are added to problem solve, to help ensure functionality, and to improve the probability of delivering results.

The same body of mapped information will be created for each primary area. When assembled, *Game-Changer* will represent the web of life mapped across the globe and framed as crisis areas needing re-wilding. In turn, the related priorities within each primary area will be specified and plans of action mobilized to meet those priorities down to the last detail.

Complementing and catalyzing this work for maximum impact is another imagination, the launch of the Climate Change/Re-wilding/De-carbonizing *PARALLEL* TV CHANNEL – a conduit for education, engaged global citizenry and action.

And why not tie it all together with even more intention by creating a Global Climate Emergency Number? When your house is on fire, you don't Google, "Who should I call?" There isn't a list of 100 contacts to choose from. In the U.S. you call 911, the "Universal Emergency Number." Three digits sets a unified crisis response in motion. You reach the 911 Control Center that houses a repository of information; maps; building addresses; fire hydrant locations; hospitals; natural gas company contacts and so on.

The response capability, police, fire engines, fire-fighters etc. are all paid for by the collective "us." It is a moment when we are all one in a crisis. And it works remarkably well.

Climate change and ecological breakdown is a crisis with a different scale and complexity. But the response to it could also be, conceptually, a 911 universal emergency-type response – unified, global, integrated, and immediate; one response with a clear mandate – Meet the Emergency. Dial 111. There is a lot to imagine here.

The degree of coordination and alignment (and money) required to accomplish all the above may seem daunting and unachievable. Perhaps, but I believe it is possible because there is an alchemy to all of this waiting for its moment.

It Only Takes a Moment.

As a case in point, from my perspective as a U.S. citizen, the December 7, 1941 Pearl Harbor attack galvanized sacrifices by all to defend freedom and defeat tyranny. Life in America was filtered through one lens – the common good for the war effort. There were scrap metal drives by children and victory gardens; rationing of gasoline, heating oil, shoes, clothing, coffee; and the sacrifices of millions of U.S. service people, of which 416,800 gave their lives. A collective brain manifested in the twinkling of an eye and an alchemy to direct the energy flow followed. It was war.

Is the climate crisis as big a threat to our way of life, to our very lives, and what we hold most dear as that infamous December day that united us almost 80 years ago?

For some the answer is "yes" and for others "no" or "I don't know." And there lies the rub. Climate change, unlike Pearl Harbor, is not a single comprehensible event with a clear enemy against which to mobilize. CO_2 is invisible and an abstraction. Global warming is a disconnect when it is -20F outside. The coral die-off on the Great Barrier Reef means what?

More than 2400 people died at Pearl Harbor. There was no ambiguity about who the enemy was or what the response should be. It was a simple 1+1=2 calculation.

For those who answer "yes" to the perceived threat of climate change, the gravity of the ongoing *"attack"* on the natural world and our planetary life support systems is also a 1+1=2 calculation. It's a Pearl Harbor situation x 100 or a 1,000,000 with a big "but." BUT without a unified crisis response to rally all of us together.

This writing appeals for the necessity of a crisis response and makes the case for how to manifest it, how to make the threat to humanity understood by many more as a devastating attack with everything that's cherished on the line. It calls to all to help create the collective brain and brawn needed to manage and direct the vast amounts of information and potential energy inherent in such an all-encompassing mobilization.

We need this unifying moment of organization and commitment that can result, simply because, although battles are being admirably won in the fight to meet the climate crisis, the war is being lost.

Moments or a Movement?

Presently, there are plenty of responses to climate and ecological degradation. There are ground-swell activist movements like *Extinction Rebellion* and *YouthStrike4Climate*. There are dot.orgs galore and NGOs and Summits and Conferences and United Nation's Committees and miscellaneous Compacts, Accords, Agreements and dire warnings.

And millions of citizen contributors.

We are surrounded by each other, running by and beside each other, constrained by discrete silos and limited by discrete actions. We are up against far more powerful forces like corporate greed and nation by nation "feel-good" pledges, political gamesmanship and calculated self-interest. And time is running out.

My aim here is not to ignore the important unifying efforts that are in motion today. More than a billion people every year celebrate the global phenomenon of *Earth Day*. *Youth Strike 4 Climate* is inspirational and compelling. The *Global Climate Strike* calls for needed disruption of business as usual. There is a lot of striving in motion orchestrated by amazing and dedicated people.

But what we have mostly are unified moments – flashes of brilliant light. What we need is a unified movement – brilliant light 365 days a year. This is the "impossible that will not fail us."

Why Impossible?

Because obviously, some would say, a unified movement reflects a naïve notion. The world is too complex. Too many organizations, too much politics, too many countries, too much big money, too many egos, too much inequality, not enough bridges to transition to a new economic paradigm, and too much disruption and sacrifice required. The obstacles are too difficult to overcome.

My response to those obstacles starts and stops with...... if a unified movement is the impossible that will not fail us then let's get on with it.

Getting on With It.

Historical researcher, Erica Chenoweth, shows that for non-violent mass movements to succeed, a minimum of 3.5% of the population needs to unite in a vocal and sustained way (Harvard Gazette, National & World Affairs, Feb. 4, 2019). Although her research focuses on outcomes related to political change and the overthrow of oppressive regimes (i.e., Civil Rights Movement; Marcos in the Philippines), it does point to the "possibility" of revolution latent in non-violent resistance/action.

Dr. Chenoweth notes that people are social animals, that change is exciting and contagious, and that the status quo can shift in perception very quickly if a sustained and compelling groundswell of resistance, advocacy and action reaches a tipping point.

I believe we can reach this tipping point by re-organizing already existing "waves" of activism such that they come to meet the shore (the masses) in more coordinated sets with their amplitude (impact) maximized rather than random one-off events and splashes of attention with relatively little, long-lasting effect.

We need these big waves: waves of the future: young people – kids – students – Millennials – Gen Xers, waves of celebrity, waves of musicians, waves of scientists and activists, waves of engaged corporations, waves of wealthy individuals, waves of united environmental organizations, waves of consumer activism, waves of leadership nations, waves of big first initiatives, waves of entrepreneurial responses, and waves of targeted non-violent civil resistance.

Each set needs to be followed by another and another – many big, all coordinated, all a part of a united movement responding to a shared perceived crisis guided by some semblance of a collective brain. The visibility of each wave set will stimulate interest, combat cynicism, evoke hope and encourage people to find their place of engagement within the climate revolution.

All orchestrated and coordinated by whom?

By the creative and organizational intelligence that manifests within the yet embryonic *PARALLEL* paradigm. I know there are seemingly endless "But hows?" or "What about this and what about that?" Those questions are natural and of course necessary, but not yet. Discovering the impossible that will not fail us requires the discipline to be patient and to suspend disbelief until you no longer have to.

This united movement wants to happen. Conditions are exquisitely ripe. Every day seems to be burdened by another cataclysmic declaration – species extinction – the Colorado River is drying up – rapid decline of the natural world. The good news, however, remains less obvious: that the potential energy, mostly invisible to us, is also expanding exponentially in response.

Potential is just that: possible, but indefinite. It's like watching something try to materialize in the Star-Trek transporter room. Can you make out what is betwixt and between?

I can. It is this *PARALLEL* climate revolution paradigm or something smarter and more impactful. It is wave after wave of children with their parents' support engaged to fight for the best future they can have, followed by wave after wave of Millennials and Gen Xers fighting for their futures, and Baby Boomers fighting for their children, grandchildren, and their legacy.

In this big transporter room, also, betwixt and between, shimmers the future Earth.

That miraculous "ball" is in our court – needing engagement and care from every one of us.

If we focus where the climate movement is weak and fix it, if we brainstorm a new paradigm to make it more unified, inclusive, and powerful, if we also keep creating moments of brilliant light, then we will fulfill our potential as human beings and we will know what is possible.

I believe it is more than we think.

Chapter 2 – Dropping Deeper into the Weeds

Imagine there are 200 critical ecological crisis or flash points, call it the "A" list. And there are 500 on a less critical "B" list and 1000 more on a "C" list. Each "hot spot" has a story that is told and the environmental impact of each is documented with some brought to life, David Attenborough style. It is all made relatable and compelling.

Examples of "A" list foci would be replacing hydroflurocarbon (HFC's) refrigerants (that have the capacity to heat the atmosphere 1000X more than CO2). Reducing food waste highlights another critical flash point. Tropical forest restoration, family planning, renewable energy expansion and addressing the complexities of managing cattle and other ruminants all require immediate and dedicated attention.

The next step crafts an IEAP (Individual Environmental Action Plan) for each crisis point with target reduction goals of *CO2* identified. It also estimates net implementation costs and projects operational savings over-time. Paul Hawken's *Project Drawdown* is already doing this with its *"100 solutions to reduce global warming."* We are well on our way.

Also, equally critical metrics would be generated to show the estimated costs to build "bridges of security" for populations adapting to changed environmental priorities and new economies. Resources would be quantified in each IEAP report to meet the needs of the poorest, the least responsible for damages, and the most affected by climate change.

Imagine that all this action is captured by a team of global "storytellers" who are social media wizards and have access to the resources of the imagined *PARALLEL* TV channel (and related social media platforms). Successes are reported as are failures. The climate fight is made transparent. It becomes easy to follow crisis points of interest. It is easy to see how to be involved. It's easy to feel part of a united movement. It is exciting to feel momentum and be hopeful.

What I am envisioning is a vast web of circulating energy and a responsive nervous system spanning the globe on behalf of the climate and the planet. Call it communication, education, and activism.

What I am declaring is that national boundaries have faded into irrelevance. Pollution, whether in China, the United States, Russia, India, or Japan, does not abide by random lines drawn on a map. The entire globe is warming, not just the countries that are polluting it the most.

The 386,000 square miles of Amazon rainforest (rainforests. mongabay.com, Dec. 4, 2020, Rhett A. Butler) sacrificed over the past 40 years to cattle raising, soybean production and logging (an area more than twice the size of California) will not obediently restrict its impact to the boundaries of Brazil, Peru, and Colombia.

Seemingly a world apart from the Amazon, about 4,500 miles, the Sierra Nevada snowpack irrigates 7,000,000 acres of fruit, vegetables, and nut production in California's Central Valley. Climate scientists have warned that it may become threatened with drought caused by guess what? – the disappearing Amazon.

And what a drought we are in the midst of in 2021. The western United States is burning up and drying out. Shasta Reservoir (that feeds the Central Valley) is experiencing its lowest levels in at least 44 years. Trinity Lake, also feeding the Central Valley, is presently half-empty.

We are connected to each other in ways that we understand and in ways that we cannot yet comprehend. What happens in Brazil, where 60% of the Amazon lies, impacts our food security, our way of life and life itself. The scale of interaction and impact encompasses the whole Earth – its climate, biodiversity, ocean salinity, freshwater availability, and sea-level rise.

As such, the scale of climate change activism must also reflect the global systemic nature of our living Earth. Dividing our actions/activism into parts and pieces limits us to un-sustained moments of impact and yields, as *The Guardian* signatories bemoan, insufficient urgency to meet the climate crisis.

So, to answer Bill McKibben's essential question asked on the cover of his book *Falter* – Has the Human Game Begun to Play Itself Out?

The answer is "yes."

<u>War</u>

Not a politically correct metaphor, but the right one.

Can war be non-violent? Yes.

Imagine if every major environmental organization across the globe embodied the spirit of dividing, conquering, and collaborating, and chose one of those 200 crisis points from the "A" list and one or two from the "B" list and several from "C."

Imagine if each one of these primary organizations collaborated with and supported other environmental initiatives that are smaller with fewer resources and are more local. And then another tier of coordinated support and another until there is a diverse community of players dedicated and designated for each hot spot.

Each crisis point would become a battle front with a dynamic leadership team all-in to win. And we the people across the globe will be the soldiers, the financiers, the protesters, the volunteers, the artists, the journalists – and when and wherever possible, the voters.

Together, we will move the climate change and ecological activism paradigm from an individual sport to a team sport to a championship league to an army.

And we fight.

The process to build these teams to meet each crisis point and to create a unified organism/movement with a plan embodies what I have called *Game-Changer* outlined above.

The weapons we fight with are our unity, our organization, our numbers, our will, our waves, our votes, our media, and our purchasing power.

Victory is de-carbonizing and re-wilding at scale.

It's simple.

But it isn't.

Chapter 3 – But It Isn't

Adding to the presumed "impossibility" of these climate revolution ideas are two undermining dynamics that stifle the forward movement of ecological restoration and climate repair.

First, many people assume that to meet the climate crisis they must virtually disappear. Cars are taboo. Planes are the enemy. Consumerism is antithetical to ecological preservation. An auto-immune response of sort happens, and we attack ourselves for just being. This dynamic can cripple if not paralyze us. It contributes to despair and cynicism, and reinforces the tendency to do nothing, to sit on the sidelines and keep things unchanged. It empowers inertia.

Second, if I am an autoworker, a lawnmower manufacturer, a coal miner, flight attendant, or a palm oil plantation worker, what happens to my future? Am I left in the dust, scorned, and forgotten? What happens to my community? What happens to the fabric of my life?

How livable is a future that is as disrupted as climate change activism appears to demand? Is that future car-less? Is there less freedom to enjoy life? Does it mean going backwards? Do avocadoes in the Northeast U.S. become a fond memory for those who remember the time before the war?

These prospects threaten to condemn us to hypocrisy; deny us our modernity; steal our freedoms; and strip from many their place in the world, particularly their economic security.

These are not hopeful prospects.

How do we sort through these conundrums?

Humanity has an undeniable environmental impact on this Earth. But that impact need not be by definition a stab in the back or to the heart of our planet. You are not "bad" for just being. We must dispel that notion for anyone carrying that burden.

The Earth is resilient. CO_2, the atmospheric gas, we primarily attribute to climate change occurs naturally. Plants and animals need it. Our respiration releases CO_2 with every breath. The oceans absorb it. Forestlands store it. Stable CO_2 levels have played a valuable role in keeping the Earth warmish, but not too warm.

What we have today holds no secret. It is a double whammy of our own making – a fossil fuels addiction that has created a glut of greenhouse gases like carbon dioxide in tandem with an assault on global ecosystems like rainforests, peatlands and grasslands that naturally store carbon.

The fix equally holds no secret. We need to burn less fossil fuel (a lot less) and we need to conserve and re-wild like crazy. And then hope we've done enough to slow down global warming.

But in any fix scenario that I can imagine, success will not look like five climate-change steps forward and zero back. It will not look like you and me never driving or flying again. It will not be a world without supermarket oranges and avocadoes in northern climes. There will be hamburgers.

How about starting right now with five steps forward and two back – a net gain of three?

Five Forward

How about an across-the-globe Marshall Plan-like commitment to fast-track green urban transport and reduce, if not eliminate the single largest source of transportation-related fossil fuel emissions?

How about a Green New Deal-like commitment here in the U.S. to connect the largest urban areas within 600 hundred miles of each other with super-high-speed rail or hyperloop routes? And in turn significantly reduce short-trip air travel and the related atmospheric pollution it causes.

How about establishing mandatory carbon sequestration rules reflecting the real costs and the real responsibilities for every kind of travel and living?

How about re-directing exponentially more investment dollars to advancing solar, wind, geothermal and tidal technologies, electrical grid-scale batteries, hydrogen fuel applications, green concrete, aviation efficiencies, alternative refrigerants and much more?

How about an immediate focus on overhauling the lawnmower and recreational vehicle industries that account for more than 5% of the air pollution in the U.S.? Running one gas lawnmower for one hour is equivalent in air pollution impact to running 11 new cars for an hour (Environmental Protection Agency (EPA) estimate sited in *Only Natural Energy*, Oct. 3, 2018). Add the pollution from gasoline-powered weed wackers and leaf blowers and you have an important piece of our 21st century living that needs to urgently change.

For anyone who might now be lurching towards a fit of apoplexy at the prospect of their beloved lawnmower being taken away, I have four things to say.

First, I love lawnmowing.

Second, there will be lawnmowing in the future, but there needs to be as few internal combustion lawnmowers as possible. We should be aiming for zero.

Third, with such sea-changes needed to be made in our "ordinary" lives comes the understanding that there are businesses and livelihoods and futures that are all married to the affected industries. This impact must be anticipated and met with both an urgent and sensible transition plan.

Four, procrastinating and delaying these necessary changes to de-carbonize is not an option.

There will be disruptions. There will be tough moments. There will be sacrifices. There are uncertainties.

And there is this indisputable fact.

There is a future Earth that we in the present are responsible for, and we should do our best to protect it for our children and theirs and theirs.

Two Back

There is no magic wand in sight to align the world with magical/enlightened thinking, even mine. We will not always go forward. We will continue to generate CO_2, but how much will we reduce it and how much will we sequester with re-wilding?

5,000,000 acres or about 8000 square miles of primary Amazon Rainforest, the so called "lungs" of our planet, were lost in 2020 (ABC News, Neil Giardino, February 5, 2021). That's 10X the size of Maui in one year or about the size of Israel or Vermont if you like. Way too much! 600,000 of those acres were from fires that scorched the Chiquitano tropical forest in Bolivia.

The numbers are numbing. The scale challenges our brain, and the fix defies comprehension. Where does the tipping point lie when the Amazon biome no longer produces enough rainfall to support its ecosystems? The answer is debatable. But what is a fact is that point in time draws closer and closer to now. What is fact is that we are in a race, actually a battle, to protect this treasure and vital organ of our planet and hopefully push that timeframe back.....to never.

What do we do?

How about half of us focus on championing the five steps forward (make it 6) and half of us focus on reducing the two steps backwards (make it 1 ½)?

On one-hand such a simplistic notion seems like an unrealizable, stupid abstraction, if not insane. On the other, it makes perfect sense.

So, what do we do? Ignore what makes perfect sense or dismiss it because it's impossible?

You know where I stand. We pick up the ball of string labeled "Perfect Sense," find the loose end and follow it as if our children's lives depended on it.

Chapter 4 – The Money

Let's dispel one rebuttal to what's possible – there isn't the money.

Yeah, there is.

There are so many ways to look at this.

How about reversing the $1.5 trillion-dollar Trump tax cut give-away (that went into effect in 2018) to corporations and the wealthiest and put that money into the green urban transport piggybank and accelerate that work 100-fold?

How about wrapping your brain around the fact that we Americans consume about 140 billion gallons of gasoline annually? Our airlines use 18 billion gallons of aviation fuel (statista.com). We burn 5 billion gallons of heating oil. We use 27.5 trillion cubic feet of natural gas. And in 2018, American coal weighed in at 691 million tons.

That's a lot of CO2. In fact, we represent 4.34% of the world's population, yet produce 14% (worldometers.info/co2-emissions/us-co2-emissions) of its fossil fuel CO2 emission.

Rather than just feeling victimized by this incongruity as in... *"WTF can I do?"* .... we need to make it work for us on behalf of the future.

How?

<u>Tax it for Starters.</u>

And use that money to transform our nation's infrastructure. Restore Midwest grasslands. Re-forest everywhere possible. Make our agriculture production regenerative and more climate friendly. Invest in "green" technologies. Incentivize "green" every-day living. Solarize intensively. We can do so much if we galvanize our will to do so.

But isn't a "Tax It" strategy a non-starter – political suicide – sacrilege?

Yes, definitely all three, if the boogey-men cards that scare and confuse people are allowed to be played unchallenged.

Remember, we are in a Pearl Harbor-like moment, possibly X 100 or a 1,000,000. We need to find new ways to move forward and prove that we are a multi-generational "can do" populace rather than offer more of the same stale excuses to stay stagnant and prove that we are not.

Taxes are not monolithically bad. Yes, they fund way too much unnecessary waste. They subsidize industries that should not have that benefit. Unquestionably, they can be regressive and unfair. And yes, they can be plain stupid. The obvious point is that there is room for improvement, a lot of room. But the most important point here requires a call to action, your action. Vote to identify and oppose waste. Vote to fix our tax policies. Make government work even if conventional wisdom declares such notions to be naive and fanciful.

<u>Invest in the Stability of the Future</u>.

And don't forget.

There is also a flip side to the idea of a "tax" that needs to see the light of day. In that light, taxes are more than just a burden to bear and resent. They are tools to harness and express our collective intention and power. They have a purpose. They have potential. They can be justified.

When we add compost to the soil to increase its fertility, that compost has a cost. Think of it as a tax, but it is really an investment, and the benefits are astronomical. That tax feeds us today. That tax will feed the future tomorrow. Without paying for that fertility and investing in the soil, we would be doing little more than mining and eventually depleting it.

Similarly, without taxing carbon and investing in the "fertility" and the stability of the future, we are robbing that future; we are depleting it; we are dooming it.

So, when those boogey-man cards are played, as they always are, by those fear mongers invested in the status quo, we can say to them, "Hell no" to our tax dollars supporting government waste, duplicative bureaucracies, unnecessary military programs, and insane cost overruns. And "Hell yes" to fighting climate change, re-wilding and investing in the greenest future possible.

We need to tax carbon smartly, justly and spend every dollar wisely. If that's part of the "impossible" that will not fail us, so be it.

And we need to reject straight-out the poverty mentality that there is no money.

Because if that were true, how did we find $1.7 trillion dollars (Esquire, Charles P. Pierce, Feb. 25, 2021) so the F-35 fighter jet could have its future? Yet somehow, we can't find the money for our children to have theirs.

Insanity.

All that said, taxes are an aside. My big climate revolution ideas do not constellate around tax policy.

Chapter 5 – Manifesting Brute Cash

There is no escape from the realities of money. Climate change activism and ecological restoration need cash and lots of it to finance de-carbonizing and re-wilding. Being a poor cash-strapped movement is not an option any longer. It cannot be an excuse for inaction, half-measures, or failure.

Government cannot do it all, but it can do a lot. To reiterate, it needs to fulfill its critical role in overhauling an unjust and wasteful tax system. It needs to legislate key policies like "smart" carbon taxation and appropriate funding to champion initiatives like the *Green New Deal*. It needs to institute progressive regulations that rapidly advance de-carbonizing. The U.S. government needs to lead by example across the globe and be a hero, rather than the climate change villain it became during the Trump administration.

Fortunately, the Biden administration is now engaged and focused on the imperative of climate change action, has rejoined the Paris Accord (despite its deficiencies), and has named former EPA Administrator and former head of the Natural Resource Defense Council (NRDC), Gina McCarthy, to be the White House National Climate Advisor.

Even with the good Biden news (may it continue) and even if the above tax enlightenment and re-prioritizations were to magically manifest, the climate revolution we need requires a lot more oomph and engagement than our government or any government can manifest – a lot more.

It needs to be, first and foremost, a from the bottom-up worldwide people's movement that showcases the spine, the will, and the urgency that politicians and bureaucracies, most often, can only react to rather than create.

We can all plainly see the fickleness of governing in the United States by Executive Order where actions and policies have the impermanence of tumbleweeds blowing hard right and left from one administration to the other.

Hence, one of the essential ingredients needed to both push forward with that urgency and be more independent from the vagaries of those tumbleweeds is what I call "brute cash" – the cash to do everything and anything to turn the tide, in haste, on global warming.

Think of it as "the people's cash." There cannot be too much of this kind of muscle.

This muscle can have a lot of different looks.

Look #1, for example, is the emergence of the *Wyss Campaign for Nature*, a special project of the Wyss Foundation that aims to conserve and protect 30% of the planet's lands and oceans by 2030. Backed up by a $1 billion investment and in collaboration with the National Geographic Society, The Nature Conservancy and many local partners, nine projects in 13 countries will receive, as a starter project, $48 million in assistance. The size of the far-reaching areas to receive this promising benefit is about 10,000,000 acres of land (about the size of Switzerland) and 17,000 square kilometers (6563 sq. miles) of ocean. The countries affected are Argentina, Zimbabwe, Australia, Costa Rica, Romania, the Andes Amazon region and the Caribbean Marine Protected Areas.

Hopefully, this signals just the beginning of the flexing of this kind of philanthropic muscle.

What could be done with $10 billion or a $trillion? That's the way we need to think and that's the kind of money we need to manifest. And I believe it is possible.

Consider the potential of Look #2. In 1985, 1.9 billion people watched the "Live Aid" concert for Ethiopian famine relief. Approximately $127,000,000 dollars (history.com/this-day-in-history/live-aid-concert) was raised through that action. In today's dollars that is $322,000,000.

More than 3.5 billion watched the 2016 Rio Summer Olympics; 2 billion watched the funeral of Princess Diana in 1997; 2 billion were on-hand for the memorial service for Michael Jackson in 2009 (Beyond the Dash Blog, April 3, 2019); 1.9 billion watched the wedding of Prince Harry and Meghan Markle (The Economic Times (ET), May 20, 2018).

How much money could be raised in our interconnected world today in a united climate activism campaign? Imagine again those big, coordinated waves of celebrity, children, musicians, unified environmental organizations, and the many others that were listed above. Imagine the 2022 - 24 - 26 - 28 - 30 Olympics all tied into the Global Climate Change movement and planning for it right now. Imagine the billions of people watching FIFA World Cup Soccer every four years also becoming engaged as part of this movement.

Why not? Aside from COVID-19, which is still a force impacting the globe now, what is standing in the way? Is it the "impossible" again?

Here is a third look.

It is the inspiration for the title of this book – *PARALLEL*.

Chapter 6 – An Introduction to *PARALLEL* //

Imagine a // economy dedicated to fighting global warming. That is, an activist economy that requires, for example, as little as choosing an alternative to what you ordinarily buy on Amazon.

Imagine a // choice for banking and credit cards. Why not make our collective money work full-time for climate change activism. Why not re-direct trillions of dollars of our purchasing power and capital for the planet and become part of the global warming solution?

But how?

We create, over time, a free market // economy with a singular focus – All *Profits for the Planet*. We unite our monies in our everyday living as a global movement. We co-operate. We identify friendly philanthropic dollars and add our own purchasing power and capital. We do the impossible. Not all of us. Enough of us.

Entrepreneurial ideas such as this need to be well matched to the readiness of the market waiting for those ideas. Without this readiness, no matter how great the idea, progress will be stalled. With this readiness, the seemingly impossible becomes possible.

The global yearning for solutions to the climate crisis is vast. The readiness for *PARALLEL* is obvious.

A // free market economy united by a single focus – global warming – is possible. Why not start now?

Getting Started – The *PARALLEL* Bank

A bank, cooperative or perpetual trust could be created as a first step. Let's call it, the *PARALLEL* Bank. A founding leadership board of directors – a wheel with many spokes of expertise – is formed.

And a simple road map to build // is crafted. Simple means principled, focused, incremental, and innovative.

The founding principles are crystal clear.

The // Bank has one focus: Global warming.

There is only one stakeholder: Planet Earth (its life support systems and all life).

It has a charter with two goals: All net profits will be directed to de-carbonizing and ecological restoration actions.

And there is one measure of success – Delivering impact.

The 30,000' View

The // Bank will underwrite a credit card – The *PARALLEL Climate Emergency Card* and offer a lending program – *PARALLEL* Lending dedicated to the purpose and vision of its one stakeholder. The // Bank will also have a charitable giving arm – *PARALLEL* Giving that provides grants to decarbonizing and restoration initiatives.

Becoming Big

Imagine the *PARALLEL* Bank growing into an international alliance – the *PARALLEL* World Bank Alliance. Its credit cards, lending programs and charitable giving will become global in scale. New foci will appear like educational initiatives. A social media platform will develop and become unrivaled.

Money equals power and energy. Too much power sits in the hands of those who are near-sighted and exploitive. Not enough energy is available to support climate change activism and planet-purposed entrepreneurship in the profound ways needed. This presents a problem. The *PARALLEL* Bank offers part of the solution. It would provide a conduit for both aligned philanthropy and consumer and commercial capital to support de-carbonizing and ecological restoration actions.

Philanthropy

Philanthropy is integral to addressing one of the undermining factors that limits access to capital for necessary climate technologies, innovations, and IMPACT programs. The inherent aversion to risk by traditional banking defines that factor.

One unfortunate result of this aversion is the so called "Valley of Death" – the desolate place that promising enterprises, who are perceived to be too risky, get stranded. Another nail in the coffin of enterprising initiatives shows up with skeptical investment professionals pricing debt at interest rates that prove to be deal-killers. A third related result is that early-stage technologies, even up and coming industries, cannot handle investments at the enormous scale needed to attract major investor players.

By force of habit the banking system restricts the financial agency needed to meet the demands of the climate crisis. As a result, too much promising potential falls through the cracks. This loss contributes to our faltering. It is unacceptable.

To address this limiting factor (risk aversion) that thwarts research and development, testing, scale-ups and market penetration, the *PARALLEL* Bank would aim to leverage philanthropic dollars to make bank lending viable to targeted business enterprises, environmental programs, projects, conservation land acquisitions and the like.

Risk cannot be ignored, but it is also a tired excuse for the status quo to persist and vital opportunities to be ignored or to languish. This is a perfect place for philanthropy to play a pivotal role as a catalyst to shift the perception of risk, enable more enlightened lending (and ultimately investment) and have much more impact than it ordinarily does in its traditional role.

PARALLEL – Climate Emergency Credit Card

The aim is to build a global climate change movement. Although it is counter-intuitive to suggest the "buying of things" as the uniter/igniter to do this, here is why it can be.

Everyone in the developed world is buying things using credit cards. You don't have to become a member of an organization to do so. You don't have to march or strike or declare yourself in any particular way. Trillions of dollars are being exchanged. Servicing and championing that exchange is a profitable banking economy. That economy, virtually the "be-all and end-all" of life on developed Earth, is the obvious genesis of our climate crisis but the not-so-obvious doorway (or at least one of the doorways) to its solution.

The // *Climate Emergency Credit Card* (backed by the *PARALLEL* Bank and eventually the *PARALLEL* World Bank Alliance) has the potential to be an instantaneous conduit to activism, a global community, and a movement. Holders will use it virtually every day. They will have impact every day. They will belong to a community around the world sharing the same intention by just being members. There could be tens of millions of cardholders.

More. Why not?

Together, cardholders will manifest, through what is ordinarily just the invisible business of banking transactions, more of the "brute cash" or the muscle needed to do the work of ecological restoration and de-carbonizing that is not getting done because there is never enough of it. With the // *Climate Emergency Credit Card*, this dynamic changes.

The aim is for the card to become a champion and a focal point for a global "Take Back the Climate Movement." In doing so, it will be a unifier and offer to many a much-needed sense of awakened kinship. It will uniquely empower millions to join hands to insist that the "buying of things" play an important role in the "fixing of things." Simultaneously and most importantly, the effort will be dedicated to transforming consumerism such that it is more aligned with the health of our planetary life support systems, the future Earth, and its future generations.

The power to generate the brute cash and have the muscle to move the entire globe is within "our" power. We don't have to wait on anyone or anything! This united movement wants to happen.

Here are Some of the Early Indicators

Presently, the Swedish financial company *Doconomy* has launched the "Do Card" which tracks emissions related to a cardholder's purchases and offers consumers options to buy carbon offsets. Also, out there now is the climate card by *Cornercard* and the *South Pole Group*. With their card, all offset costs are covered by the card itself.

Today, there is also an established way for not-for-profits such as the Sierra Club or World Wildlife Fund (WWF) to offer their own credit cards. It is through a commercial banking enterprise known as "Charity Affinity Credit Cards." The Bank of America World Wildlife Fund card, for example, donates $5.00 for new cards and $5.00 for card renewals. In addition, 0.23% of consumer purchases on the card goes to the WWF.

On the one hand, it is heartening to know that the climate and not-for-profit credit card is more than another big idea. On the other, how do we make it more impactful and engaging than I took a trip; I paid for it with my Cornercard; they bought carbon offsets somewhere for me; I feel less guilty? How do we improve upon a financial model that only returns $2300 to the Sierra Club on a million dollars of card sales?

To be clear, what's in place is important because directionally it's a step. It represents a growing consciousness. But what is in place is not generous enough. It is not urgent enough. It is not ubiquitous enough.

What would a new credit card paradigm look like that was not largely dedicated to the profitability of the credit card companies, but rather dedicated to meeting the urgency of the climate change and ecological crisis?

How could this revolutionary card be capitalized? What might make it an attractive proposition to the ESG (Environmental, Social, Governance) investor universe that uses more enlightened socially responsible metrics to make investment decisions? What are other creative paths to access capital and financing? What would make the // Climate Card compelling to millions of consumers worldwide and help deliver the brute cash needed in the immediate term to stand by the life support systems of our planet?

Maybe the // Card charges only a "recommended" $50 a year instead of $90 or more? Maybe the interest rate is always 5 points lower than standard card charges? Maybe the card is tied to a consumer discount program made possible by participating supporting businesses. Maybe the card uses a piece of its capital to invest in, for example, for-profit solar utilities or regenerative farming operations? Maybe the *PARALLEL* TV channel that I mentioned earlier receives some of its operating funding from the *Climate Emergency Card* revenues?

What I'm certain of is that this is not the moment for business-as-usual. What I know is that the heart of the solutions to the problems we face lies in our numbers, our votes, our courage, our faith, our unity as a mighty bucket brigade and our collective brute cash.

All tied together is how we will make a difference.

// PARALLEL Lending

PARALLEL Lending is the foundation for a more enlightened expression of capitalism. Why not transform as much of our economy as possible with a dynamic *PARALLEL* lending arm? That is, lending solely dedicated to supporting ecological restoration and de-carbonizing action.

Why not take aim at challenging the axiom of perpetual growth by offering an alternative to it?

We do this by deploying a significant niche of capital available to // Lending and make it work for the planet/us. We do this by financing new choices for millions around the globe who are anxiously waiting for new, more enlightened ways to plug their lives into sanity. We give those, who want to stand apart from the lemming stampede they find themselves entrapped in, more ways to do so.

The only way to do this is to create the financial wherewithal to support an economic paradigm that will do the transformative work of values-driven entrepreneurship. And this needs to be done with a Marshall Plan-like dedicated focus.

It is not the strongest of the species that survives, nor the most intelligent; it is the most adaptable to change.

– Charles Darwin

Will we adapt in the face of faltering and lacking the urgency needed to protect our planetary life support systems?

PARALLEL Lending is one good hopeful reason to answer, "Yes."

// PARALLEL Giving

The need is obvious, and the premise is simple – direct a portion of *PARALLEL's* "profits" to support global activism campaigns in every major affected eco-system. There are myriad possibilities, so priorities would be identified, and meticulous focus applied for maximum impact utilizing the granularity produced by the work of the *Game-Changer* agreement and its global climate action plan.

For example, the *Global Mangrove Action Plan* mentioned in the *Game-Changer* Road Map (Chapter 1) would inform the grant funding decisions by *PARALLEL's* global giving team. Another place *PARALLEL's* global activism efforts might focus on is the development of solar throughout the developing world. This could be a complementary grant program to *PARALLEL's* lending initiatives.

Other places of *PARALLEL* activism might result in the acquisition of large tracts of critical habitat around the globe and the underwriting of initiatives/programs that help to reduce local economic pressures in critical bio-regions that lead to deforestation, over-fishing, species extinction and other ecological stress points.

As the // World Bank Alliance establishes itself, the reach and IMPACT of its Global Giving campaign will expand.

Reality Check

PARALLEL does not exist. It's an idea.

Global warming is accelerating. The usual suspects are to blame – a powerful fossil fuels industry, wasteful consumerism, planned obsolescence, and myriad other shortcomings attributed to our 21st century living.

Something else stands out. Climate activism impact appears to have hit a wall. Although public awareness and angst about global warming has grown dramatically, activist leaders like Bill McKibben, Naomi Klein and Greta Thunberg all bemoan the fact that our planetary life support systems are more imperiled than ever. The sum of the prolific actions of environmental organizations, the inspiring worldwide climate strikes, the attention-grabbing youth-for-climate rallies, high profile lawsuits, and the many celebrity activists are all proving to be not enough. We are faltering.

How does the activist community navigate around or through this obstructive wall? How do we make haste to change the narrative from our faltering to altering the advance of climate change?

The change needed is two-fold.

First, climate activism needs to become more causal in transforming our economic system to reflect its sustainable values and goals. To do so means to stop deferring to the "old guard" that dominates the global flow of money and to create a parallel "new guard" that serves as an independent force offering new choices and representing more enlightened social values, financial influence, and economic leadership.

Second, we must energize the vast amount of resigned, cynical, and uninformed human potential (including its capital and buying power) haplessly sitting on the sidelines of everyday living and unite it, empower it, and put it to work for the climate. When meaning and purpose are shared by millions, anything and everything is possible.

Our faltering will begin to end when we find our way to manifesting these two understandings.

PARALLEL offers a vision to begin a conversation to do this creating.

Chapter 7 – The New Confederates

The climate deniers, the resistors, and those firmly entrenched on the wrong side of history will not come to their senses in time, if ever.

The reaction to the *Green New Deal (GND) Resolution* illustrates this in spades. This *Resolution* should, in principle, be a no-brainer. De-carbonize as fast as possible. Champion economic and social justice. And protect and care for people who will be most impacted by the transitional upheavals as we move away from fossil fuels.

What could the problem possibly be?

The naysayers to this kind of societal imperative and moral intention are not unlike the champions of the Confederacy back in 1860. I call them the "New Confederates," not because they are pro-slavery or overtly racist, but because they betray morality, they defend ignorance, they stay loyal to big money, they lust for power, and they normalize racism by protecting and abusing their white privilege at the expense of the disadvantaged, as if it were their right.

Climate change and slavery are different monumental issues 160 years apart with different battle lines in play. But both are defined by catastrophic human failing characterized by greed, contempt for others, and willful ignorance, with a better world for all hanging in the balance.

And like slavery, climate change deniers must also be overcome. There is nothing more compelling today.

Some of the Battlelines

One battleline constellates around the following assertion. "*The Green New Deal* (GND) is a destructive, socialist daydream." We should all get used to this "socialism" scare tactic. No doubt the word has been focus grouped to death. It's a very effective weapon for those on the wrong side of history because it is so easy to apply. Just the mere mention of the word casts the dark shadow of government control. One of the intended links is, of course, to communism. People naturally fear and reject such a prospect, whether unfounded or not.

In fact, *The Green New Deal* has zip to do with "socialism" in the pejorative sense that the New Confederates intend. Although a total red herring, the link works to evoke fear and distrust. It closes minds. Rather than being, at long last, a breath of fresh air and hopeful leadership, the *GND* resolution becomes a threatening evil prospect. A battleline is clearly drawn here and those on the right side of history better be prepared to put the socialism, democratic socialism (and communism) labels to sleep.

Another weaponized phrase used to attack the *GND* is – "Massive Government Take-Over." The strategy is simple. Misdirection that evokes fear works. Again, it closes people's minds before they can be informed. It assures ignorance and adverse reactivity to necessary societal changes and increases, if not guarantees, the likelihood of climate disaster.

The *GND* is not a mutant fungus. It has nothing to do with taking over our government and everything to do with championing democracy and governing and getting something done, sadly a lost art in Washington DC.

What the New Confederates camouflage with their propaganda is a real attempt at a massive government take-over – their own!

Although the Trump administration is historical, its counter-to-the-facts, regressive New Confederates ethos is alive, emboldened and certainly plotting to re-gain power. As such it is instructive when looking ahead to connect the following dots.

When a prospective leader and his or her minions ignores most of the world's climate scientists, advocates abandoning the Paris Climate Agreement, is intent on undermining the Clean Air and Water Acts and thinks pulling the plug on improving auto fuel economy standards is a good idea – that's the kind of take-over that should be alarming.

When your government chooses to be impotent and legislates virtually nothing but tax breaks to corporations and the wealthiest private individuals – that's a take-over to mobilize against.

The *Green New Deal* is good at its heart. When the resolution is fleshed out, there will no doubt be plenty to debate. But what is certain is that the *GND* is striving to meet the world ethically, responsibly, and positively.

The other side, represented by the New Confederates, need not be reflexively demonized or de-humanized. Some may be wonderful parents, grandparents, and community-minded citizens. There may be talented artists among them. Some may have a great sense of humor. But equally, their public policies and deceitful propaganda, expressed as the rejection of climate science, the undermining of environmental regulations, the perpetuation of systemic racism and social injustice, and the abhorrent treatment of migrants and those seeking asylum remain tragically and unforgivably rotten to the core.

So, don't think for a second that this is not war. It is. The New Confederates must first be defeated and second be skillfully convinced to support // despite themselves.

There is a *PARALLEL* confection idea introduced in Part 3, Chapter 23 that will do this – guaranteed.

<u>A World without McDonald's and Ben & Jerry's?</u>

Another corrosive battle line used as a scare tactic ominously declared that the *Green New Deal* would cause the number of cows in the U.S. to go from 94,000,000 to zero. Translation – the end of hamburgers and ice cream and the beginning of the apocalypse. This is, of course, nonsense. But can you think of anything more galvanizing to turn public opinion against you than the prospect of a hamburger and ice cream-less world, a world without McDonalds and Ben & Jerry's?

There is no denying that farming practices can be destructive. Industrial scale feedlots, pesticide use, agricultural run-off into waterways, antibiotic over-use, and excess tilling present serious problems. But farming can also be restorative. The Regenerative Agriculture model can help to reverse climate change by rebuilding soil fertility, minimizing tillage, and sequestering carbon.

So, don't take the bait. Cows have their place in a *Green New Deal* future, perhaps even a prominent one. First, let's flesh out the *GND Resolution* and see what there really is to eat rather than feast on provocative and speculative fears that are counter-productive and undermining to a future most of us want.

Please don't get hung up on the name *Green New Deal*. My aim is to not champion it per se but rather to make the point that, whatever a progressive legislative climate action initiative might be called, it and those who support it will be demonized by the New Confederates' vitriol.

Chapter 8– Business-as-Usual

Part of the cynicism that greets me when I talk to others about my climate activism ideas stems from the disheartening contempt for our capitalist economic system. The gist is there is no hope for the Earth as long as profit-making drives our everyday lives.

This argument has legs, but it is also complicated. We shouldn't fall into oppositional camps without at least understanding each other.

For example, Arizona, one of the sunniest places in the U.S., gets only 8% of its energy from the sun. Why? Let's go all the way down the rabbit hole with this one to see if there is a bottom,

One argument makes the case that the state's biggest utility, Arizona Public Service (APS), a subsidiary of the publicly traded Pinnacle West Capital Corporation, has historically opposed solar. Why? Because the for-profit driven Pinnacle West has other important investments in nuclear energy and fossil fuel generation, and solar power potentially represents a threat to their profit-making plans for the present and the future.

But this reduction is incomplete and not fair.

Counter to the above, Pinnacle West is, in fact, investing in solar energy with 100 megawatts planned by 2025. Additionally, 850 megawatts of large-scale battery storage are in the queue to meet future demand when energy usage peaks, particularly after the sun sets. That's 950 megawatts of new clean energy technology.

Therefore, we can't simply drop Pinnacle West in "the climate be damned" capitalist corporation box.

However, counter to that counter is consideration of the 2018 ballot initiative, Proposition 127, that would have amended Arizona's state constitution to require electric utilities to use renewable energy for 50% of their power by 2035. Pinnacle West actively supported 127's public defeat.

Arguably a big chance to take a significant renewable leap forward presented itself here. And chances are all we get in this war of climate action to meet the global warming crisis. There are no happy-ending guarantees. Maybe we should put Pinnacle West in that box after all?

Perhaps, but not yet.

Prop 127's intended 50% renewable target also had an Achilles heel that left it not only vulnerable to attack and defeat, but also with valid public concerns. What would the cost impacts be to consumers to reach that 50% target, given the many subsequent demands on APS to maneuver its energy assets to meet what would have been a constitutionally mandated action?

Consider also the capabilities of the electric distribution grid for this kind of renewable transformation as well as the related costs to update it, if not overhaul it.

It is right here where our rabbit hole drops precipitously into darkness.

Opponents of Prop 127, like APS, easily exploited the uncertainties of these cost repercussions to its customers because consumers carry the actual costs of the grid and its operations. Nothing galvanizes resistance to change by consumers more than pocket-book issues.

Here lies the darkness.

The real cost impacts of Prop 127 were decidedly unknown. For example, would meeting the constitutional mandate have required APS to prematurely off load costly assets such as its Palo Verde nuclear generating station in Maricopa County? And with what consequences and costs to consumers who would have to ultimately foot the bill? APS and its allies leveraged this scary uncertainty.

Looking back at Prop 127 in 2018 and now looking ahead, who should do this analysis and answer consequential questions that will either make or break the momentum to de-carbonize or make or break the economic viability of a utility which in turn might drive the cost of power to consumers through the roof? Without a definitive answer in real time to these complex questions, the Prop 127 vote was subject to politics, big money, and polarizing rhetoric on both sides of the divide. It was defeated and so was climate action on a scale and in a timeframe that would have set an example for the rest of the country.

In this darkness of not knowing the consequences of big change, who should be trusted? The Pinnacle West Capital board room whose fiduciary responsibilities likely guarantee that profit-making is paramount? Or the climate scientists and activists trying to prevent or at least forestall the failing of our planetary life support systems?

We ask the wrong question when its genesis stems from an economic paradigm that is failing us. What is the relevance of Pinnacle West's rate of return in the context of climate catastrophe? What is the relevance of the cost of a gaping hole in your or rather our sinking boat if there is a way to fix it or at least keep it afloat?

Both questions are irrelevant until a new equilibrium or a new normal show up that meets our climate reality as it is today, not as it was before the crisis was understood. This means change and sacrifice. This means that consumers cannot be frightened into being short-sighted and voting against what the science tells us needs to happen. A safety net is needed for them.

"Nose down. Landing gear up." If you are on board with this metaphor, the rhetoric that there isn't the money to do what is needed must stop. What there isn't enough of is the will and leadership to meet the crisis. We need audaciousness. We need bravery. We need heroes. The 50% renewable target is not a "wouldn't it be nice," it is a must.

Also, and not to be overlooked, Arizona needs Arizona Public Service. It cannot be driven into the ground, but it can be driven to the ground. No one can defend "Massive profits (again)," which APS earned, according to a May 2019 article in AZ Central, in this moment of climate crisis. Even "decent rates of return" should be on the chopping block. Business-as-usual must die a quick death or life as we know it will.

Is this quick death impossible? Perhaps, but only because of our assumptions, our perceptions, and our habituated thinking. Other than that, there are plenty of imaginations such as *PARALLEL* to challenge the disruptive arc of climate change that is making alarming headlines around the globe every day.

And who knows, maybe the change we fear in anticipation is not the bitter pill we expect.

In the meantime, the backdrop to this tug of war between the possible and the impossible is the pathetic pace of decarbonizing.

Prop 127 was headed in the right direction with its objective to hasten the use of renewable energy. There was a missed opportunity to meet its Achilles heel with creative and groundbreaking problem solving rather than tired excuses and regressive tactics hailing from an aging economic paradigm that no longer works for planet Earth and its residents.

I remain unsure whether Pinnacle West and Arizona Public Service deserve to be dropped into "the climate be damned" capitalist corporation box. But I am sure that they continue to play by the rules of that old and failing paradigm, no matter how praiseworthy those 950 megawatts of new clean energy technology.

There are no medals for second place in this tug of war. We are all winners, or we are all losers.

Prop 127 delivered a defeat for all of us on the planet. The organizers need to pass along the lessons they learned. The next battle will take place somewhere else tomorrow and the day after and the day after that. We cannot afford to reinvent the wheel each time. We need to leverage this failure and all others to plan for future successes.

And no matter what, we cannot accept that 8% or 20% of power from renewables in Arizona is sufficient. We must be much smarter tactically, more resilient, more strategically financed and we have to be ready to push back hard against business-as-usual.

My aim here is not to get deep into the weeds of a pro and con debate on economic philosophy. In any case, we have what we have to work with, manage and transform. We have capitalism today in most of the Western economies, so it does little good to bemoan what is or what is not.

<u>I Lied. Into the Weeds a Little Bit.</u>

Capitalism does not doom us to outcomes or expressions of greed, amoralism and environmental catastrophe, in much the same way that many genetic mutations do not doom us to contract any given disease. It is possible, perhaps in some situations probable, but not a fait accompli.

The field of epigenetics considers genes and their expression, in other words, why and why not some genes express themselves in any given individual. For example, 45% of women with the BRCA 2 gene mutation will develop breast cancer by age 70 (National

Breast Cancer Foundation, *BRCA: The Breast Cancer Gene*). This obviously presents a significant and concerning percentage, but my point here is that the majority of women will be okay despite the mutation.

Similarly, the predisposition to thoughtless opportunism in order to make a buck may be a problematic capitalist behavior, but not necessarily. There are other variables that influence the kind of expression we see.

Unfortunately, in both cases, epigenetics and capitalism, we do not know exactly what turns on or off a gene to manifest any given disease or what misleads a mind to make or not make abhorrent and immoral choices for the sake of personal gain and financial profit.

But clearly, human behavior can corrupt any economic system or any presenting situation. In the case of capitalism, there is a broad range of degrees of behavior possible, ranging from outright evil such as ivory poaching to Certified B Corporations that are dedicated to using business activity as a force of good.

PARALLEL aims to be one of those forces of good despite the economic system within which it may be classified to be functioning.

The tendency to reduce complexities like genetics and entire economic systems to certainties reflects either ignorance, misguided assumptions, or entrenched hopelessness. Whatever the reason, it does not serve the greater good because feeling doomed and powerless makes the present disappear. And in life, the present, and what we try to do within it, counts the most.

Post-script and a Reminder

The 2018 Arizona ballot initiative was a two-steps backward moment, no matter what side of the fence you were on – for or against. We perceive the illusion that there are two sides to this fence, because fences, by nature, divide and that is what we expect. But not this one. When it comes to planetary life support systems, there may be fences, but they do not divide. There is only one side, the one we are all living on together.

But also, good news and big steps forward soon followed. The Navajo Generating Station near Page, Arizona, one of the nation's largest coals plants and polluters, shut down in 2019. That generating capacity is now being replaced with cleaner natural gas from other power plants (Mesquite and Gila River) and solar arrays and battery storage.

Remember, five forward – two back.

Chapter 9 – A Return to Hamburgers

It may be true that the most expedient way to make money in the world of beef cows and hamburger comes through industrial scale feedlots.

However, that cost efficient and profit-making production system is accelerating the depletion of carbon stores and increasing atmospheric methane and nitrous oxide. And on top of that, feedlots increase the likelihood of water pollution due to agriculture run off from unvegetated ground and increase the risk of creating antibiotic resistant strains of bacteria due to a production system that relies on the over-use of antibiotics to be successful.

What is the real cost of accelerating the production of global warming gases like CO_2, NO_2 and methane to society as a whole? What is the real cost of water pollution? What is the real cost of reducing the effectiveness of antibiotics to each and every one of us? Are any of these incremental costs factored into the real cost of beef production?

The answer is no. If they were, I suspect feedlots would fail as the most expedient way to make money in the world of beef.

There needs to be a reckoning here and in turn a disruption of business-as-usual. Feedlots and Concentrated Area Feeding Operations (CAFOS), where a 1000 or more cows are confined for 45 days or more in an area without vegetation, need to be phased out.

Will the capitalist ethos allow this to happen and support a transition to a regenerative agriculture model? Are we confronted with an inevitability that it will not; do we surmise that no one is going to voluntarily surrender their right to cheap hamburger, thereby damning the climate and the environment?

There is no "inevitability" to our human behavior. What remains certain is our human potential for glorious triumph or abject failure and everything in between.

The end of capitalism does not stand as a pre-condition for accelerated re-wilding and de-carbonizing. It is not the solution for us to stop our "faltering."

The solution lies within the magic that we are capable of creating: from the Sistine Chapel, Korsakov's *Flight of the Bumblebee*, the

Hadron Collider, artificial knees, Live-Aid, to the Fosbury Flop. What can't we do?

I can think of a few things that exceed my imagination or my embedded psychological constructs. But none are related to re-wilding and de-carbonizing our world as if the future depended on it.

Time to move.

PART 2

The "35 Emails Trail" to the Valley of Death

Chapter 10 – A Warning

In the beginning, there was no *PARALLEL*. Instead, I imagined what I called *The First Climate Emergency Bank* and the *Climate Emergency Credit Card*. Thanks to the arduous 35 email slog below and in turn my 9-month residence in the Valley of Death, the *PARALLEL* you will read about in more depth in Parts 3 and 4 was born.

I have changed most of the names and related organizations in what follows, with one exception. Those specifics are not important, but the email content is verbatim and valuable.

The exception is Bill McKibben, author and founder of 350.org who sent me two of the thirty-five email replies along the way. I admire Bill. He is a climate champion and the inspiration for this *PARALLEL* effort of mine. I hope we will meet in the future and work on this together.

Even if *PARALLEL* is a brilliant idea, brilliant ideas do not suffice to deliver the impossible. You may soon share the sentiment, as some of my early readers have conveyed, for me to leave the forthcoming personal email journey behind, which slowed down their read. "Just get on with bringing the *PARALLEL* conception to life," they urged.

I have decided that I cannot do this. I think that slowing down is necessary, but not because I want you to hear my sad stories or because I think that they have some entertainment value that makes my authorship more compelling.

Every idea seeking to answer the question, "what is the impossible that will not fail us?" goes up against a force like gravity. Let's call it the "SO-SO-Force." "SO-SO" for Same Old-Same Old. It is invisible. It is ever present and seemingly invincible. It is the force behind declarations like "there isn't the money" and insuations that engendered the fears and divisiveness undermining Prop 127 in Arizona. It is the force that pushes us toward silos, sides, sameness, and separation. It is the force that breeds cynicism and defeatism. But unlike the force of gravity, which is immutable here on the planet surface, this SO-SO-Force is not. And few seem to know this. It can be resisted and even overcome by a superpower we each have: the power of our "free-will" as human beings.

Free-will gives us the choice and capacity to transcend the constraints of our human nature, as well as our personal, social and cultural histories, and our ingrained habits. Lemmings do not have this super-power, which makes their collective stampede to the cliff's edge and over still puzzling, but not preventable. We humans do have this power which gives us the choice to veer away from the climate cliff that faces us now.

Coupled with another super-power, our "skillful-will," we have the capacity to not only make these transcendent choices, but also to skillfully connect them (using our intelligence, creativity and adaptability) to actions that can realize just about any aspiration.

Choosing to deliver on "the impossible that will not fail us" falls outside of anything and everything that is usual, predictable, expected and accepted. If I were writing the "Idiots Guide to Saving the World" or the "5 Easy Steps to your *PARALLEL* Life," the emails that follow would be unnecessary. I would have already figured everything out for you to consume. But I haven't arrived at that destination. And you need to understand why so that my mistakes and misjudgments potentially serve as useful guideposts for your successes in the future. Also, these emails show various aspects of this SO-SO-Force and its mysterious ways, and my efforts laid bare to apply my free and skillful wills to meet it.

So, please take this journey with me to the Valley of Death – highs, lows and in-betweens guaranteed. Inspirational insights and tedium, like any trek, also appear with certainty. The Valley, also known to me as the business graveyard, is the place where entrepreneurs, dreamers and champions of any given cause land when they miss their target or hit it to no avail and crash in disappointment.

Yes, I was crushed to land in this Valley. But if there is any blame to be cast it is, on one-hand, mine for not conforming to reasonable expectations and, on the other, the force of inertia (aka the SO-SO-Force) for not bending to my inspirations and earnestness.

In any case, without the Valley detour, *PARALLEL,* as I am presenting it, may have never been discovered.

Much of my journey was uphill and rocky. Much of it was bushwhacking. There were few vistas. And the ones that did appear, disappeared quickly. As a result, I am posting this warning at the "35 Emails" trail head.

Warning:

The trail ahead is unmarked and slow, but it is the one I took for better and for worse.

Chapter 11 – It is All Bill's Fault.

I know the Valley of Death. We are not strangers. I have been running from it for my entire entrepreneurial life.

I did move. I did follow my own dictates. But apparently, I did not run fast or ably enough. Because I am in the Valley right now with the framework of my big *PARALLEL* ideas to change the world lying ingloriously in a heap...at least seemingly so.

Will I be able to reconstitute them with another burst of energy?

Or will I leave all that I have imagined behind as a carcass to keep company with the millions and billions of other ideas, humble and grand, across the millennia, rotting into oblivion?

What happened?

<u>Let's Brainstorm.</u>

It started in April 2019 when I randomly read that open letter in *The Guardian* newspaper signed by my Vermont neighbor Bill McKibben and 22 other climate change luminaries.

To rehash, their gist was simple and alarming to me. All the activism, all the organizing, all the organizations – all of it around the globe – was not creating the urgency needed to prevent the collapse of our planetary life support systems.

Perhaps I exceed in naivete. I expected Bill and his cohorts to offer some inkling of a responsive plan of action to this unbelievably dire assessment that we are going down the tubes. If not them, then who? Could it be that everything that is in motion, all the transformative intention– the strikes, rallies, lawsuits, lobbying, countless environmental organization supported by millions of contributors, legislation etc. – adds up to less than zero?

Engaged in disbelief and alarmed, I wrote to Bill on April 23, 2019. Although we had never met, as it turned out, he knew of me. I will tell you why in a minute. Portions of my email to Bill are below.

***

<u>#1</u>

"Hey Bill, have you glimpsed a wormhole that gets us to "sufficient urgency" faster? Are there ideas that you've imagined or heard of that have seemed impractical/unattainable, yet necessary? Would they, could they be transformative solutions if only there was a way?

And if there isn't an imagined way yet; if every effort to put the pedal to the metal is in motion from your vantage-point and the outcome remains as it is "insufficient," then I want to be a part of a brainstorm. I want to join the expedition to find the wormhole that leads to this illusive urgency."

***

As I typed to him, I thought to myself, "Bill, will never write back. He is probably inundated with random rantings. He's too busy. I am wasting my time."

***

My April 2019 email to Bill continued.

"Bill, I dreamt of organic baby food in 1976 to grow the fledgling organic foods farming paradigm and reduce the use of pesticides. I hadn't yet seen a bald eagle back then and after reading Silent Spring, I saw the window closing. Eleven years later, the first jars of Earth's Best baby foods were produced. It happened.... and it still is.

Like many people, I ask myself, what can I do about the Climate Crisis, given that everything I can think of doing, I'm striving to do?

Today, I'm writing to Bill McKibben. I'm asking, regardless of whether we're past the tipping point or not, how do we get to "sufficient urgency?" Will we get there by Thinking globally and Acting Locally? Will we get there by ending capitalism? Will we get there by somehow unifying the Climate effort? Will we get there with an exponentially bigger pot of money?

What is being missed? What assumptions are in place that are self-limiting? What actions lead to that wormhole?

I know you've written a library on the subject. I know you've tried to answer the questions I'm asking. I know you signed the recent open letter in The Guardian. I understand the net of Climate Action today is insufficient. (And I fear letters like this drive you crazy.)

Unless you believe, we're in effect, in a hospice or remedial situation, and heroic actions to save the "patient" as we've known it are futile, what does "heroic" look like and how might we get there faster?

Let's brainstorm.

***

The Scenic Road to the Valley

Bill wrote back to me on April 24. I waited less than a day. Astonishing.

#2

"(Ron,) you might enjoy the last section of my new book, Falter—it tries to address all this at some length.

thanks for your good work—bill"

***

Bill knew me or of me because of *Earth's Best,* the company my brother Arnie and I founded in 1987. It not only had its own measure of prominence as the first organic baby food company in the US, but also because we started it in Middlebury, Vermont, Bill's stomping ground as a Middlebury College professor.

In any case, I picked up a copy of *Falter* anxious to feel more hopeful.

I read it and did not feel more hopeful. In June 2019, I wrote back to Bill.

***

#3

Bill, per your suggestion, I have been reading Falter.

As you write, "the key (to the future) lies in how we see ourselves. Are we playing a team sport or an individual sport? The answer seems to dictate which way the climate change chips fall."

(Bill), the fact is we play both types of sports and sometimes at the same time. We recycle and we drive a gas guzzling Dodge Ram. We have solar panels on our roofs, and we globe trot around the world on vacation. We belong to environmental organizations, and we live in the country or suburbia and drive everywhere for everything.

(Bill), what will drive us to the ethos that "we're all in it together," to solidarity? What will "organize the world" in such a way that there is sufficient urgency to overcome "knowing cynicism," die-hard individualism and undermining resignation?

How do we advance the ubiquity of solar panels and build a super-charged non-violent movement on behalf of everything we hold dear?

Is it fantastical to think that there are answers to these questions obedient to the time constraints we seem to be faced with?

My interests are all related to these questions. I think the (scale and complexities of human behavior x the scale and complexities of our earthly ecology x inertia x entropy) pushes us towards the edge of comprehension.

We default to manageable/comprehendible silos which seem to be failing to create sufficient urgency to sustain our planetary life-support systems and seem to limit us to winning battles, but not the war.

It feels like we are in uncharted territory. How do we explore that?

***

In this June 14, 2019 email to Bill, I also sent him a more detailed attachment laying out some of my thinking in more depth.

And then Bill delivered on my expectations. He did not respond.

I was disappointed, but still fresh enough with enthusiasm for my developing ideas to meet head-on the failing/faltering culture of climate change activism. The Valley of Death did not feel nearby. It was still out of mind and out of sight. It was the mountain top I was heading for. That is all I could see.

***

On August 14, 2019, I sent this email to Bill (in part).

#4

Bill, I wrote to you on June 14. My effort was probably too lengthy. Perhaps you did not connect to it.

I am trying again.

Why isn't there the urgency needed to prevent our life support systems from spiraling into collapse?

I have reduced this complex question to a simple answer. Climate change activism is not yet a unified global "movement." Rather, we are united in global "activist moments" like shooting stars that flash with striking brilliance and then fade away. The distinction between a "movement" and "moments" is not a subtle one. It is like the difference between a complex forest ecosystem and a number of trees randomly planted here and there.

The 2016 Paris Agreement disappointingly stands out now as one such shooting star, a moment with great possibility that has remained largely unfulfilled. I imagine that the upcoming "Strike for the Climate" will also be a "moment." Remarkable and necessary, but also likely to fade as an action.

The overriding hope, of course, is that all these "moments" will add up to the needed urgency to stabilize planetary life support systems, but what's the timeframe for that metamorphosis?

Similar to the limitations of "activist moments" are the constraints of "organizational silos." There are numerous environmental organizations like yours, 350.org., Green Peace, and World Wildlife Fund that do amazing work, but the paradigm they all play-in, albeit expansive on one-hand, is also by nature and necessity narrowly focused. Each organization is locked into its own membership campaign, fundraising strategy, and areas of focus (or turf). Each organization is arguably akin to a "moment." Absolutely necessary, but in total, so far at least, not sufficient to generate the urgency needed.

In any case, the activist paradigm in place is failing us. I do not have the authority to make that assessment. But you and 22 other notable activists do and have done so.

What I'm saying Bill, in response to this fact, is that too many people do not know how to connect to the climate crisis. The residue of this disconnection ranges from cynicism to despair to avoidance. My own wonderful, accomplished children, now in their mid 30's suffer in some fashion from these maladies. They scoff at the futility of "moments" of action and feel victimized by the "evils" of capitalism.

I believe there are tens or even hundreds of millions of people who care immensely about this Earth, but who are sitting on the sidelines as dis-empowered spectators, isolated from each other and passive witnesses to "moments" they believe will make no difference in combating climate change.

All this inaction, all this potential energy represents the needed urgency to potentize the impact of climate activism. What's missing is an accessible "movement" to belong to day-in and day-out, something bigger than "moments" passing by.

I would love to sit down and discuss this with you.

***

More Silence from Bill

You must be ready for this. My outreach was again probably too long. I figured Bill was incredibly busy. And to repeat a familiar refrain living within my psyche, who the hell am I?

But maybe Bill's silence also reflected part of the underlying problem. Climate change activism, like celebrity, has a bubble-like quality. That bubble is well insulated, almost like a private club. It is hard to get inside.

In any case, when you are on this type of journey, nothing allows for hindsight. You don't know if your every move leads you toward the mountain top or toward the Valley of Death. There is a lot of second-guessing yourself. Did I say something wrong? Are my ideas totally impractical?

It takes an act of faith to keep investing time and energy into the dark.

The reason I could and can, despite rejection and/or deafening silence, goes back to the fact that my crazy organic baby food idea in 1976 was not so crazy. Why can't it be "me" who has had a revelatory insight or a game-changing idea, even if I'm not an expert or one of the insiders? Why not me?

Why not you?

In any case, I believed in my ideas. I thought that they possibly offered an opening to an elusive doorway that would prove invaluable in advancing climate activism and meeting the global warming crisis.

It is not arrogant to dream, to believe in yourself and to be hopeful. Who can say what magical thinking is? Being wrong is also okay.

Looking ahead, I would write to Bill again on February 5, 2020, sending him a summary of my *Climate Emergency Credit Card* idea. Interestingly, Bill would reply on February 18 - *"This strikes me as a fascinating idea."* More on that in a moment.

The bad news was that Bill had left me in the doldrums as the fall of 2019 approached. The good news was that my twin-brother Arnie engaged with my climate initiative efforts.

Long story short, Arnie's networking efforts led us to Woorim Hindan, the president and CEO of the Los Angeles based Akash Social Enterprise. ASE is a social investment fund that, in part, employs the idea of "integrated capital" to fund social entrepreneurs working to solve complex social and environmental problems.

Eureka! Right? A perfect fit.

We introduced the same *Climate Emergency Credit Card* concept to Woorim (that I had presented to Bill) in a tight 3-pager on November 18, 2019. You can find this in Addendum A.

Below is Woorim's promising reply on November 19 – a one day wait!

Chapter 12 – Woorim

#5

Dear Arnie, Dear Ron,

What an honor to receive this thoughtful proposal. Thank you.

I am in complete agreement with your diagnosis and analysis and am very much interested in the initiative you suggest. The financial system, by extension the banking system and our concept of money is built on extraction and self-centeredness. If we want to support healing the planet and communities, we can't do that with a broken financial system.

While Akash Social Enterprise is practicing this new way of working with money – and has done so for 35 years – we are not a bank and do not issue credit cards. There are interesting and relevant players in the banking industry (Amalgamated, who bought New Resource Bank, Beneficial State Bank and Aspiration), all of whom fill only part of the need. If you don't already know Aspiration, I suggest you read up on it since they have an interesting concept of incentivizing sustainable purchasing behavior through their card.

You mention that you would like a bank to be not-for-profit. ASE is a not-for-profit organization. That has many advantages, and it is worth exploring charitable status for a bank. A difficulty for a non-profit is how to raise growth capital. That said, I'd suggest focusing on how governance (who decides, towards what purpose) can be separated from economic ownership (the commons, shareholders, cooperative ownership etc.). The governance piece is critical: the bank you envision should have a voting board seat for Mother Earth for example. And one representing communities affected by climate change, one for employees etc. and maybe one for investors. Just a couple of thoughts on how to be the systems-change we want to see.

I'm excited to explore this idea both with my ASE hat on as well as personally. As a matter of fact, I've had some conversations with ASE board members about the need to establish a truly regenerative bank. Would it be helpful to gather a number of people around this idea to carve out next steps? I believe that Tim (co-founder of ASE) and Allen (retired CEO of ALD Trust) and potentially someone from the Global Alliance of Banking on Values GABV could be interesting thought partners.

How can I help?

All the best,

Woorim

***

Arnie and I could not have hoped for a more positive reply. It is a heady feeling when you think you are clearing obstacles, dodging bullets, and getting somewhere with your expressed dreams and inspirations in the real world.

We replied on November 21, 2019.

***

#6

Dear Woorim,

Your enthusiastic and supportive response is very welcome. And your offer to help and engage with others in your network to explore what may be possible is needed and greatly appreciated.

The effort that we are envisioning will take a "village" of committed and talented individuals to manifest.

The Amalgamated Bank and related Aspiration Bank websites are heartening. Every stated aim – Do Well/Do Good – Save Money/Save the Planet is easy to align with.

And yet there is something fundamentally lacking relative to the aims of the Climate Emergency Bank and Credit Card that we are envisioning.

Specifically, our aim is to focus on climate change and the universe of activism related to it. And to direct this laser focus towards building a very visible and sustainable movement that connects the global population to ecological restoration and de-carbonizing actions 24-7-365.

Critical to our definition of success is maintaining disciplined focus; establishing a populist movement; and building extraordinary visibility. These three elements are missing from our first impression of the Amalgamated mission.

A fourth element that we deem very important is to establish a not-for-profit enterprise. We understand the viability/practicality of achieving this remains unknown currently, but it is our aim.

And it is our aim because, so far, what we discern is that most ESG supportive entities (for-profit banks, public and private investment funds, companies, etc.) are constrained by ROI expectations and enrichment of shareholders and executives.

The social and environmental results are, too often, either "light" in substance, impact, and commitment, or worse some version of "greenwashing" that satisfies shareholder expectations but fails to address with urgency the climate emergency.

We are in pursuit of the manifestation of an idea that will, like nothing we are aware of, bring diverse populations (national and international, socio economic, political, religious, etc.) together to fight for the future which we imagine is collectively holding its breath hoping and praying for something like this to finally happen.

Whatever the organizing and financial structure is, it needs to deliver to the fight what we are calling "brute cash" to overcome, what is too often, a confounding scarcity of resources in the hands of the people and organizations on the front lines of trying to catalyze needed change.

As you suggested, governance is critical, and we agree. Directionally, the ideas you suggested for board seats i.e. Mother Earth; communities affected by climate change; employees, etc. are the type of thinking that is needed to create an entity that can bring about the deliverables that we together can and will imagine.

We are ready to meet with you, Tim, Allen and everyone you think would take an interest in learning more and exploring with us what is possible. You pick the location, and we will be there.

Best regards,

Ron and Arnie Koss

***

And the meeting happened on January 23, 2020. I flew to Los Angeles from Vermont. Arnie flew from Maui. We put together a dynamic Power Point and did our best.

After returning home I wrote to Woorim on January 27, 2020.

***

<u>Still Hoping...and Still on the Valley Road</u>

<u>#7</u>

Dear Woorim,

Thank you for inviting us to ASE. The meeting with you and Allen was informative, stimulating, and enjoyable. It has given us a lot to think about.

The story unfolding here on Earth is a dire one. I think we all agree the "possible" is failing us. The task now is to discover the "impossible" that would not.

Although many questions remain, two certainties persist in our minds. Big, bold, and extraordinary actions are needed now. And we are on the right track with the First Climate Bank (Author's note: This name pre-dates the PARALLEL Bank) and Climate Emergency Card focus.

Arnie and I are looking for fellow collaborators who share our focus, values and offer complementary and catalyzing skill sets to enable speedy progress and results.

There may be reasons to think that we are aiming too high or lacking in the requisite experience or cash resources to be successful. We understand this assessment. The very same confronted and confounded us as we strived to transform the baby food landscape and grow the organic foods industry 30+ years ago.

Perhaps the fit is with you and ASE or alternatively a for-profit offshoot of ASE with ASE as an investor. Perhaps there is no fit with anyone until Arnie and I demonstrate more solidity than we have, such as cash commitments behind our ideas.

If so, the question then is how much time will be lost questing for money that is in abundance to do the obvious that is profoundly needed?

Woorim, any additional thoughts and input you may have will be greatly appreciated. Please provide us Allen's contact info as well as Gary's.

Arnie and I will do our best to continue to move forward.

Best regards,

Ron Koss & Arnie Koss

***

Woorim replied on January 29, 2020.

***

#8

Thank you, Ron.

It was great meeting with you and Arnie, and I'm honored that you consider ASE as a possible collaborator for your big and bold vision. Thank you for making significant journeys to meet with Allen and me. I'm copying Allen here, who can provide contact information for Gary and Pete.

I agree with you, the needs and challenges driven by climate are very clear. The mission fit with ASE is also very clear. At the same time the ideas of a bank and/or a credit card need more contours. Although ASE is a lender, retail banking and consumer credit cards are unknown territories to us. One idea that comes to mind is to commission a preliminary analysis of the opportunity, develop the business case, identify the funding needs etc. A 'learning journey' with bankers such as Allen, credit card processors, climate non-profits, activists etc. The conclusion of that initial phase will get us clarity on what it will take and who the best fit partners are (which may or may not include ASE).

What ASE can provide is to help find someone who can conduct the initial phase, provide them with a docking point at ASE, coaching by me and my team. We would need funding to support that work and pay someone to do the research and write the report with conclusions and recommendations. An initial $50,000-$100,000 would get us off the ground. To be clear, ASE can give recommendations but would expect you to do the fundraising for the project.

Please let me know your thoughts.

Warm regards,

Woorim

***

Sigh and SO-SO

Sigh. Woorim drew a line in the sand, a familiar line that declares that there is an "us and them." In an instant, Arnie and I moved from the feeling of everyone sitting on the same side of the table looking at the same existential climate crisis to Arnie and I sitting across the table from Woorim looking at who would assume the financial risk to take another step forward.

It is not that Woorim was being unreasonable. My aim is not to knock him. It is just that ordinary reasonableness is not responsive to a crisis. The ship is sinking. Two of the crew have an intriguing, unproven, but potentially life-saving idea. And yet the money-people on the ship are debating the cost and the related risks to giving the idea (of which they are enamored) a shot. Rather than recognize the relative insignificance of their financial risk and stay attuned to the immediacy of the sinking ship crisis, the money-people ask the two crew members to find the money themselves, while of course cheering them on.

This is the SO-SO force at work doing what it does best – obstructing – dividing and conquering. This undermining force works hard every day. These email exchanges demonstrate that clearly.

To be clear, Arnie and I were not looking for an investment in our idea so we could make money off it. We did not have an ownership stake in mind to capitalize on our intellectual property and entrepreneurial chutzpah. Rather, we were freely offering our ideas to anyone/everyone, no strings attached other than to retain the integrity and intention of the impulse.

Naturally, we were disappointed. There would be no "easy street" – not even when it was needed the most.

What to do? Reflexively, as we had done so many times before in our entrepreneurial lives, Arnie and I mobilized ourselves into "lemonade-making" mode with the following reply email to Woorim.

***

#9

January 31, 2020

Thank you, Woorim, for the response and input.

Your suggestion and approach to a "learning journey" seems sensible to us, particularly if it is timely.

To be clear, Arnie and I have a singular focus – this climate emergency project. We understand that ASE is a lender, and that retail banking and consumer credit cards are uncharted territory for your organization. Due diligence is naturally essential. And it is for us as well.

We understand and respect that, within most organizations, there is a range of appetites for risk. Start-ups are defined by assumptions and projections and therefore are indisputably risky. It would be helpful to understand your thinking on what would make a foray into this uncharted territory of retail banking be an acceptable risk for ASE.

Arnie and I concur that we need to do the fundraising for this "learning journey." And we appreciate and recognize the value of what you are offering to support the advancement of the work.

With this understanding and given the potential value and importance of advancing this work, please consider the following proposal.

To get started, let's set the initial target of fundraising to be $50K. We would ask ASE to make a grant commitment of $12,500. This would offer a significant amount of prestige to the effort. Arnie and I would be responsible for raising the additional $37,500. Having the ASE commitment in-hand would help us be successful with this first big step. In contemplating this, we wonder if the additional contributions could pass through ASE's 501c3?

Once we have the first $50K in-hand, Arnie and I would be responsible to put the second $50K together. Our experience (and we're sure yours as well) is that the first money-in is the most difficult. With some substantive demonstration of momentum, we are likely to then quickly be successful getting to the $100K target.

Woorim, this is a practical way to move forward. We understand that your starting point is for Arnie and me to do all the fundraising. In principle we agree with you, and we are also trying to get this project in motion ASAP. The $12,500 grant would be a kick-starter that would be immensely helpful. We are not asking for anything other than what we believe is needed to move forward with prudent haste.

Again, thank you for considering this.

***

Perhaps you can feel the desperation in the above reply. Arnie and I were all but begging Woorim to help us get started. We knew where this exchange had been transported us. We were now captives in the realm of risk averseness – the anti-oxygen environment that leaves entrepreneurs gasping for (any) possibility. What we needed from Woorim was a leap from his rational and prudent mindset to a more impulsive and responsive one that would meet the imperative of the climate crisis and align more with his expressed personal sentiments.

We were so close. We could hear the Earth angels cheering us on. And we thought Woorim was also so close to that leap, to escaping the gravity of an economic system that with few exceptions and no matter what the pronouncements of social responsibility garnished around its hard core, preserves itself.

But obviously, not close enough.

Ironically, the notion of preservation across the spectrum of capitalist behaviors is futile when the true view of the forest through the trees today is climate catastrophe. It does not matter how much money you spend or save or make when climate extremes accelerate and the underlying macro-equilibrium, that we all count on to assure basic securities like food and shelter, begins to flicker, as it is, with uncertainty.

Status quo thinking and decision-making appears ludicrous when this "flickering" becomes embedded in the marrow of your bones. I am Exhibit A for this mindset. But when it is not embedded as such or there are constraints (real or assumed) and you are removed from the adrenalin rush of the "all hands-on deck" amygdala, a hurdle of $50,000 or $100,000 becomes, as it did for Woorim, a bridge too far.

The fact is every corporate, governmental, organizational, and institutional action of preservation suffers from an irredeemable narrowness when not responding to the global climate crisis. The ship is sinking. The multitude of parlor games going on within it – for example, the ones that build our 401Ks or trade commodities or clear rainforests to raise cheap beef and soy – day by day slip closer to the water line, much like our coast lines.

What has been and remains most consequential as an arbiter of success in our capitalist economy – return on investment (ROI) – stubbornly inches towards irrelevance. And what has been historically invisible or not relevant, like CO_2 concentrations, rises now consequentially to the nth degree.

Arnie and I were discouraged. But we were also buoyed a little bit by the reception to our *Climate Emergency Credit Card* inspiration.

Also, another hopeful thought occurred at that time. It had been almost six months since we had reached out to Bill McKibben. Why not try again? What the heck.

Chapter 13 – Bill + Woorim to the Rescue?

<u>#10</u>

February 5, 2020

Hi Bill,

Please take a look at the 3+ pager attached below.

Many of us are scanning the horizon to make a difference, to not falter. You've made it clear of the potential make-or-break impact that banks, asset management firms and insurance companies can have on the fossil fuels industry.

My brother Arnie and I have been exploring for the past 6 months another potential impactful leverage/pivot point within the consumer and possibly commercial banking sectors. The prospect is empowering because it doesn't completely hang on overcoming institutional inertia.

We want your input, and if this engages you as we hope, we want to put our heads together with you and others and make a plan for next steps and action.

Best, Ron Koss

***

How likely would Bill respond to the *Climate Emergency Credit Card* idea? Also, ten days had passed since our January 31 email to Woorim without a word – not a good sign. On one-hand it felt like we were now shelved in cold storage. On the other, hope springs eternal in the heart of an entrepreneur.

Arnie and I did the only thing we could when in the doldrums. We gave Woorim a nudge.

***

<u>#11</u>

February 10, 2020

Hi Woorim,

I hope that you found our proposal engaging and are considering its merits.

Arnie and I are organizing our approach to raise $87,500 of the $100K estimate that is projected. We are ready to move on this and believe we will be successful.

Would appreciate an update and any related questions you might have.

Best regards, Ron and Arnie Koss

***

Woorim's response below was timely and encouraging.

***

#12

February 12, 2020

Dear Arnie, Dear Ron,

Thanks very much for your response - and thanks for the subtle reminder. Before we decide on who/how to raise money, I suggest you have one more conversation.

I'd like to introduce you to Amy and Ben (copied here), fellow change makers who work for the not-for-profit Spinning Foundation. ASE and Spinning have a strategic partnership and share a philosophical inspiration.

They could be an excellent partner to work on the learning journey I suggested. Even more relevant: they've been working on designing a stakeholder-governed climate bank. It all sounded so familiar that in the spirit of emergence and because time is precious, I propose that the four of you schedule a call to compare notes.

Dear Amy, Dear Ben,

Please meet Ron and Arnie Koss, two remarkable and inspiring entrepreneurs with a vision to build a bank with a climate mission.

Please let me know how your conversation goes.

Woorim

***

Arnie and I were of the mindset, whatever Woorim wants, Woorim gets. Maybe this was a fork in the road that went somewhere.

It did not.

I will spare you the exchanges because they are too same old – same old.

***

Bill Roars to Life.

Bill responded to our February 5 *Climate Emergency Credit Card* email with the uplifting email below. The Valley Road has many such moments. Of course, in this moment, there was every reason to respond hopefully. Because you never know. But I am writing now with that hope being a distant memory.

***

#13

February 18, 2020

This strikes me as a fascinating idea. I couldn't tell if you were interested in partnering with existing banks or starting your own. If it's the former, I'd connect you up with folks from places like Beneficial State or Amalgamated, who we're working with on the campaigns against Chase et al.

thanks for good thinking

bill

***

#14

February 20, 2020

Bill,

Arnie and I would like you to connect us to the folks at Beneficial State and Amalgamated. Thank you for offering us that introduction.

Regarding "our" good thinking, I fear it will be too little, too late unless it is united now with your good thinking and Paul Hawken's and Naomi Klein's and the good thinking of many others of like mind who have achieved prominence through their life's work and achievements.

Practically, what do we do given reality such as it is? Who isn't over-committed with their own priorities?

Arnie and I believe there is a way. You do what you can do. Maybe that means just prominently lending your name to voice support. The same may be true for Paul, who we know is immersed in writing a follow-up book to Project Drawdown. In the same vein, Arnie and I will do what we can do. Maybe that's living in the trenches for a while incarnating "our" good thinking because it's our focus and we can.

Climate activism needs money and lots of it; that's indisputable. It's obvious to us that to do this there needs to be a united, high profile catalyzing initiative that drives money on scale much more effectively to do the work of de-carbonizing and ecological restoration.

The merging or consolidation of the good thinking of the highest profile climate activist leaders like yourself such that it is perceived as a dynamic and unique force will do this. We can claim our power as a movement right here by grabbing capitalism with authority and redirecting it rather than being victimized by it.

Money is the great equalizer. On one-hand, the "love" of it is arguably threatening our planetary life support systems. And on the other…. Bill, that's the problem. The "other" hand is relatively weak.

It is the collective "we," the millions who are engaged in some way as activists; the millions sitting on the sidelines feeling dis-empowered and cynical; and the millions who are ready and willing enough to engage but haven't found a way into participating…. Bill, it is this collective "we" that represents the other hand that wants to emerge as an expression of the love for this Earth and a counter to the love of money.

If we do not falter, it will be because the human potential represented above coalesced as a united climate activist movement. It will be because all the purchasing power represented above was leveraged to the max to finance de-carbonizing actions. It will be because more and more of the "buying of things" was re-directed to support natural resource conservation and ecological restoration.

Amalgamated Bank may prove to offer an invaluable pragmatic stepping-stone to get all of this good thinking in motion. But it will take much more than Amalgamated to realize the scale of impact that we are aiming for and that is needed.

Bill, can we meet for an hour sometime in mid to late March to brainstorm and explore all of this in more depth?

Best, Ron Koss and Arnie Koss

***

Ask for what you need. We needed this meeting with Bill. Little did we know that COVID-19 was about to wreak havoc with our everyday normal lives. Personal meetings were all but going to disappear from the face of the Earth. In any case, Bill wanted to wait and see how Amalgamated would respond to us. What a difference it would have made if he had engaged with us and our "fascinating idea" rather than watch from afar with curiosity. This is not a petty complaint or whine. The difference between success and failure is often a thin margin. How do you build momentum? How does the impossible become possible?

It could have, should have happened when one of the top 10 influencers in the climate activism universe went to bat with us. Arguably, an unrealistic and perhaps unfair expectation of Bill McKibben, but realistic expectations and outcomes are failing us.

Nonetheless, we were grateful because Bill did engage, and he did introduce us to someone in his network. It was a breakthrough. Our world was expanding with new possibilities. Arnie and I were hopeful, because you never know where and when that special dime will show up that life turns on.

With Bill providing us his contact info, Arnie and I introduced ourselves to Josh Allen at Amalgamated Bank's Sustainability Division. By the way, Amalgamated is the largest Certified B Corp in the United States.

In anticipation I had a stream of fantasies of all the amazing things that could happen. It is not all bleakness on the Valley Road. Also,

I am naturally inclined to only imagine success. I knew better, but it didn't matter.

Chapter 14 – The Unraveling

Is that the Valley in the Distance?

#15

March 6, 2020

Hi Woorim,

How do we move forward in earnest?

Three thoughts on the matter.

First, Arnie and I presented a proposal to you to put the money together to invest in the learning journey. We would like to learn what your thoughts are on this.

Second, you and Allen were going to connect us to the climate bank initiative that is focused on financing solar installations. Will you still do this?

Third, Mike Bloomberg spent $400+ million on his presidential aspirations and Tom Steyer $150+ million.

Woorim, is there any question in your mind that the money is out there to take a smart risk on transforming banking and credit card ownership on behalf of climate change activism? Is there any question in your mind that this is an imperative?

And if you have no question and you see an opportunity for ASE to lead and to grow (your fund) those couple of zeros, how can the risk be managed to justify being out there on the leading edge?

If the possible is failing us, what is the impossible that would not?

Time is indeed precious. How do we move forward?

Best,

Ron Koss and Arnie Koss

***

Arnie and I were clearly frustrated at this point. As seasoned entrepreneurs, we knew from experience that Woorim was energetically disappearing. It made no sense. We were so allied.

But this reflects the time we are in. The "No Sense Era." The time when the most biologically rich savanna in the world and a huge carbon sink, the Brazilian Cerrado (3X times the size of Texas), is being razed to produce soy, beef, cotton, and sugar cane, and the time when United States lawmakers can find $1.7 trillion dollars to invest in the failed F-35 fighter jet (The Inquirer, April 1, 2021) but procrastinate about funding high-speed rail.

Think about this craziness. AMTRAK estimates that the cost to replace its existing Northeast Corridor (457 miles) with true high-speed rail amounts to $500 million per mile (Forbes, April 15, 2021, Adam Millsap). At first glance, this stated amount must be a typo. The cost is obscene. But let's put this high-speed rail cost per mile (which isn't a typo) into the context of the F-35 debacle. A quick calculation (by me) shows that $1.7 trillion dollars buys 3400 miles of high-speed rail or more than seven Northeast Corridors installations.

What are we doing? This is OUR $1.7 trillion wasted; OUR sacrifice; OUR ambivalence; and OUR disempowerment. How do we explain this failing to our children and our grandchildren?

Well, all Arnie and I could do is reach out to Bill's contact, Josh Allen, at the Amalgamated Bank and hope for that lucky dime to miraculously show up so that this craziness would have something to turn on and the world would be set right.

No Lucky Dime...Not Even a Lucky Penny

And we did reach out to Josh with one of our personalized, yet now standard, introductory emails.

Arnie and I then had a cordial follow-up call. Unexpectedly, Josh had a negative view of credit cards – no lucky dime or penny in sight. As I recall, he saw the whole credit card interest rate structure as exploitive, and we couldn't budge him off that disposition. Very disappointing.

But he did listen to our pitch. He was engaged which Arnie and I appreciated. And there was also no doubt that we were facing another stiff headwind, if not a hurricane one. In some respects, the call was and felt like a courtesy favor to Bill McKibben. And it highlighted once again the formidable disadvantage to being outsiders.

Nonetheless, when you are in lemonade making mode, you keep hoping and trying. Part of that effort was to push back a little and introduce Josh to an innovative credit card established in South Korea.

Also, Arnie and I took keen note of Josh's mention of Marilyn Waite, the Program Officer in Environment at the ($11 billion in assets) William and Flora Hewlett Foundation. A quick Google search revealed this provocative information. Marilyn managed the foundation's grantmaking on climate and clean energy finance with the ambitious goal of addressing climate change by accelerating the transition to a climate-friendly economy. Maybe we were headed in Marilyn's direction. From what we read, Marilyn and the Koss brothers were on the same page.

***

#16

March 12, 2020

Josh,

Ron and I appreciated your engagement today and hope there will be future opportunities to continue the discussion.

Please check-out the follow link: https://unfccc.int/climate-action/momentum-for-change/ict-solutions/green-credit-card-i-republic-of-korea

This card reflects some of the potential that needs to be captured in the credit card space but not all of it. It's a start.

Ron and I will review the document Marilyn Waite authored and will follow up with you.

***

Josh in turn asked us to take a look at another credit card that he thought might be relevant to our impulse called the Serengeti Card. And then shortly afterwards he passed this spark along to us from Marilyn Waite.

***

#17

March 16, 2020

Ron and Arnie, this (below) is from Marilyn. She didn't want to be in the middle of it but was aware of this effort underway and encouraged you to connect with them.

This may not be what you are looking but I also talked with Beneficial, and they would be interested in a collaborative conversation.

Josh – put your Bill McKibben/credit card friend in touch with this Serengeti card guy. I think he has some data/numbers.

***

We appreciated this encouraging engagement from Josh and Marilyn, but we also discerned a problem. Arnie and I were being viewed as business guys trying to get into some kind of business, altruistic or otherwise. After all, apart from philanthropy, what else could we be about? Good question. What other template or lens was available to view our climate action queries and initiative? This is a tough box to escape.

In fact, Arnie and I had no aspiration for a personal upside. *"Please take our ideas. Improve upon them. Bring to life the potential to displace and/or transform the financial power structure that has been driving our planetary life support systems towards the point of no return. Just don't sell out. Don't make it about you."*

***

#18

Hi Josh,

Trust you are well and adapting to the new, very strange (COVID) normal.

Arnie and I would be very interested in a collaborative conversation with Beneficial. Please advise as to how to advance this.

Regarding the Serengeti Card, you are correct. It is not what we are looking for.

Let me explain why, starting with the reference to Marilyn not wanting to be in the "middle of it."

Arnie and I are not trying to get into a business. We are not looking for ownership, for executive positions, for personal opportunity etc. From our vantage-point, there is nothing to get in the middle of.

We are collectively in a global crisis of climate and ecological breakdown, no less a threat than COVID-19; arguably far greater. However, the impending collapse of our global life support systems does not translate as well as the immediate threat the virus poses to our individual lives today.

Arnie and I comprehend not only the problem of failing to de-carbonize and restore critical environments like grasslands, mangroves and peat bogs. We are also imagining how to evoke a more COVID-like response to meet the climate crisis with far more urgency and impact.

We are convinced that "business-as-usual" will fail us and the Serengeti Card strikes us as just too much of that. Yes, it is greener and directionally positive. But a game-changer, we do not think so.

Arnie and I are aiming for a game-changer. And we are hoping to collaborate with others in a Manhattan Project type mindset to break new ground and accomplish this.

Naturally, during our recent call, we took note of your generally unfavorable view of credit cards. Arnie and I recognize their negative aspects and impact. But a card can be much more than a tool to facilitate purchase transactions, offer rewards or track carbon. It can be much more than a revenue line on a P&L.

Given their global ubiquity, why not explore how to leverage social media and offer a card not just to facilitate transactions, but as a conduit to build a global community and movement? Why not make the raison d'être of a credit card (and bank) to lead with purpose and build an economic engine that attracts millions and generates billions to finance de-carbonizing and ecological restoration?

We are not naïve. We understand business. But business also needs to understand us, the collective us and the collective needs. There may be nothing standing in our way to create new realities, but old assumptions. Bill McKibben and many other thought leaders and climate activists believe we are faltering. We have to keep trying.

If the possible is failing us, what is the impossible that would not? This is the question of our time. Arnie and I are looking for collaborators and for people open to imagining what we can create together. And then giving it every chance to succeed and make a difference.

Best,

Ron Koss and Arnie Koss

***

There Must be a Way.

#19

March 22, 2020

Hi Woorim,

It's been 2 weeks since Arnie and I gave you an update.

In these 2 weeks, COVID-19 has turned our personal and societal world upside down. We imagine ASE is now in a virtual day to day mode. We hope you, your family and those at ASE are managing and staying well.

Big, immovable blocks of our everyday living have moved. Uncertainties are uniquely presenting themselves. Priorities are re-arranging themselves. The impossible of yesterday is today's reality in incomprehensible ways.

Amidst this COVID chaos is also certainty. Climate change is accelerating. There is no pause button on it.

We are all experiencing the disruption of this unfolding global virus pandemic. And it may be just beginning. What will the disruption look like if our planetary life support systems falter?

Here's a brief update on our work.

Bill McKibben re-engaged after another outreach to him, encouragingly writing to us that he finds our ideas "fascinating."

Bill introduced us to Josh Allen at the Amalgamated Bank. Josh is sympathetic to our efforts and supportive, but, like you, is somewhat unsure what to do with something that is so outside of what he normally responds to.

Josh contacted the Beneficial Bank on our behalf, and they have now expressed an interest in having a conversation. He has also introduced us to Marilyn Waite, Program Officer for Climate Finance at the William and Flora Hewlett Foundation.

I think the most important take-away is that Arnie and I are onto something. You and Allen had a glimpse that piqued your interest. Bill McKibben and Josh, from Amalgamated, have allotted some of their precious time to us. Beneficial responded to Josh's outreach to them and our 3-pager with a "yes, we are interested." What we are envisioning is hovering in the collective unconscious. It wants to be born.

Many of us understand, and to use Bill's term, that we are faltering. We know that immovable blocks of our everyday living need to somehow dramatically move to slow global warming and avoid catastrophe. Perhaps, we think they can't, or we don't know how to move them. It's seemingly impossible.

COVID-19 is proving the limitations of our thinking. It is calling into question any assumptions we might have as to what's immovable or impossible. Although the analogy is not a direct overlay, you get the gist.

Woorim, please stick with us. Please be a part of the brain trust that helps find a wormhole or at least a short cut to accelerate de-carbonizing and ecological restoration. We know your hearts in the right place. You have invaluable experience. You are an important spoke in the wheel. Allen is an important spoke. The wheel needs spokes, many of them.

Who can see what's possible and act upon it, if not the people with the consciousness, experience, and privilege to do so?

***

#20

March 28, 2020

Hi Bill,

We hope you, your family and community are managing and staying well.

Here is a brief update on our Climate Emergency Credit Card and First Climate Bank work.

Arnie and I are receiving "interest," in our ideas, but interest is not enough. It can go on forever without results. Another take-away is the reminder that banks and bankers are risk averse. We know this first-hand.

What moves the needle from interest to action? What shifts the banking community's perception of risk from unacceptable to acceptable? The answer may be simple.

Bill, we think it is your buy-in and Naomi's and Paul's and the community of activists, scientists and prominent environmental organizations trying to find the path that leads us away from faltering. It is your collective voice urging millions of concerned people to become part of a global movement to harness and re-direct their trillions of dollars of purchasing power and capital for the planet that will alter the perception of risk.

Without your formidable collective prominence on-board, the "comfort" investors and bankers need will be slower to coalesce. Progress will stall. And the activist community will remain in the back seat while the "grown-ups" in control of the money stay in the front seat doing what they do on their own behalf.

To make money work for climate change activism with COVID-like impact, we need to reclaim the power we give to banks to control our money for largely their own benefit. We need to create orders of magnitude of more opportunity for people to "purchase, lend and invest for the planet," focused on de-car-bonizing and ecological restoration.

Amalgamated is not adequately doing this work. Aspiration is not. Beneficial is not. Few have heard of these banks. They barely have a public presence. The urgency needed for tectonic change is lacking; the same urgency, you and 22 others declared is missing last April (2019) in your open letter to the Guardian.

The right leadership with the right focus can grab hold of a much bigger piece of our financial system and make it work in myriad ways on behalf of climate activism.

Finally, to re-emphasize, our sole intention is to do what we can do to act in service of the greater good. We will not succeed without you and others grokking the potential of the seeds we are trying to sow and helping them to sprout.

Bill, we hope you will engage further and explore what's possible with us.

Best,

Ron Koss and Arnie Koss

***

Life had dramatically changed with the advent of COVID. Woorim's energy had been disappearing for some time. COVID only accelerated that. Our plea to Bill above was so compelling in my estimation but it added up to nothing. I understand why. Arnie and I discounted the impact of the entire progressive banking hierarchy despite knowing that, in toto, it does a lot of praise-worthy work. But if "a lot" does not equal enough, then whatever doing "a lot" means, needs to be questioned and challenged. No reward follows clearing 2 feet of a 3-foot-high electric fence.

And that is where we stand. The doing "a lot" status quo may be laudable and satisfying to many who are participating in that good work. Nonetheless, it is plainly failing us.

Chapter 15 – Another Shooting Star

<u>A New Star on the Horizon</u>

Arnie and I knew from our Earth's Best lives that at some point an entrepreneurial quest takes on a life of its own. What follows below illustrates this. I felt back then in that first COVID-19 spring of 2020 and continue to feel that Marilyn Waite is a kindred spirit. She gets the critical importance of wielding philanthropy as a potent tool to help traditionally conservative and constrained financial institutions manage their risk. How do you shift the focus of investment to a bold climate-centric model? Leveraging philanthropy is part of the equation.

I think Marilyn "got" us. I just wish she had joined us more directly in building the *PARALLEL* paradigm that is now the crash site I am staring at in the Valley of Death.

Below and thanks to Marilyn Waite at the Hewlett Foundation, please find the first outreach from Lewis Draper, a leader at *Next Gen Power*, a not-for-profit funded, as we understood, by Hewlett. *Next Gen* supports diverse entrepreneurs to drive innovation and build equity into the global clean energy economy. It has created a global network of incubators, accelerators and ecosystem builders.

Certainly, there would be a place for *PARALLEL* in such a conception. Right?

***

#21

April 22, 2020

Dear Ron and Arnie,

Hope you're both well and safe. Your email was sent to us by Marilyn Waite, the head of Climate Finance at the Hewlett Foundation.

We are keenly interested in your Climate Emergency Credit Card concept, and its journey looking forward.

Peter Neal, Program Director, and I cover Climate Fintech at Next Gen Power – a clean energy network of accelerators and funds covering over 29 countries. We are currently working alongside the Hewlett Foundation as part of their "Climate Finance Strategy" to build out a Climate Fintech Accelerator program. Given the cross section of climate, finance, and fintech found in this credit card idea, I thought it might be wise for us to connect.

We're building this global accelerator program in Europe, China, and the US, and its key focus is to foster companies at both seed and growth stages - and position them for adoption or M&A by the financial industry. The goal is to accelerate the success of existing climate fintech startups and grow new ones to help mobilize significant capital towards decarbonization.

It would be wonderful to discuss this project and ways to work together in greater detail.

Let us how a Zoom call looks for you over the next week or so. Looking forward to connecting!

Warmly,

Lewis Draper

Next Gen Power

***

#22

April 30, 2020

Hi Lewis,

Thank you for zooming with us yesterday.

A couple of post-meeting thoughts Arnie and I want to share.

In the framework of B.R.A.V.E (big, risky, audacious, visionary, exponential), what we are envisioning and trying to articulate is all of that.

And arguably, a lot of B.R.A.V.E. is going to be needed to do the grand scale of de-carbonizing and ecological restoration work in front of us.

Also understood and emphasized within Hewlett's "Climate Finance Strategy 2018-2023" document is that a massive re-making of the global economy is going to be necessary to reduce greenhouse gas admissions by 60% ASAP.

How is this going to happen? One thing for certain, in our view, is that it will not be "business-as-usual," "thinking-as-usual," or "acting-as-usual" coming to our collective rescue. That said, Lewis, you made an especially important point in our conversation.

Our shared goal is de-carbonizing IMPACT. Scale is inevitably crucial to this. Getting boxed-in by idealistic principles and rigid thinking would be as self-defeating as being co-opted by undermining compromises. It's ultimately a balancing act. There is no better teacher to learn how to navigate such challenges in the real world than by being in the real world executing a big, risky, audacious, visionary and exponential business such as Earth's Best Baby Foods.

When you get to be almost 70 years old, as Arnie and I both are, you realize that there is a poignant parallel between the global warming crisis we face and our own personal lives. Time is running out. It's running out for us and by most accounts it's running out for our planetary life support systems and life on Earth as we know it.

Arnie and I have interfaced with quite a few people in the last 6 months, Josh Allen, at Amalgamated, Woorim Hindan at Akash Social Enterprise, Bill McKibben and so on. Without exception, all are accomplished, engaged in important work, committed to environmental activism in one form or another and intrigued by our vision and ideas. Setting aside the disruptions caused by COVID-19, everyone is also (so far) too busy and marginally available to engage with yet another thing.

This unfortunately is the perilous reality for big ideas. This is the plight of B.R.A.V.E. start-ups and their entrepreneurial champions. And this is why the Hewlett strategy document is so impressive and relevant to us. The authors write, "our approach is designed to address investment barriers that hamper financing individual projects all the way to portfolio investments. We do so by awarding grants to 1) instigate both immediate and long-term impacts on stimulating finance for climate change mitigating activities 2) demonstrate the efficacy of such approaches to solving climate change."

Arnie and I have a keen sense of direction. Although our ideas have engaged the interest of a discerning group of thought-leaders focused on finance and global warming IMPACT strategies and policy, we know we are headed towards facing the very investment barriers the Hewlett approach is designed to address. We know we will need one of those small grants or something akin to that to move forward.

Organic baby food is a no-brainer today, but in the early 80's it was a "pie-in-the-sky" big idea.

Uniting consumer and commercial buying power and capital at scale into a movement that finances climate change mitigating activities is another big idea that needs to happen. One day, it will also be viewed as a no-brainer that should have happened 50 years sooner when the first Earth Day was celebrated.

Arnie and I see a great potential for essential change on a global scale. Solutions at scale with this kind of potential are rare. Paul Hawken stands out as an entrepreneur and visionary trying to impact at scale with his Project Drawdown. But he is not focused on finance and its potential to re-shape our world including support for his important work.

We are not building careers. We are not chasing big bucks. What we've put in front of you and others is not about us. It is about finding the illusive pathways to support the integrity and resiliency of our planetary life support systems. To do this, as catalysts and start-up champions, we need help.

Best,

Ron Koss & Arnie Koss

***

Arnie and I were not holding back anything at this point. Bill was in a far-out orbit of the Koss planet. There was no reason to think he would be leading a landing party to the planetary surface any time soon. It seemed that we had lost Woorim. Josh led us to Marilyn Waite at the Hewlett Foundation who then led us to Lewis Draper at *Next Gen Power*. But Josh also led us away from his universe at the Amalgamated bank.

***

Sigh and SO-SO #2

#23

May 4, 2020

Ron and Arnie,

It was nice to chat last week about your history in business and vision for a future planet. I agree that there are some concrete steps to be taken to evaluate this landscape and create a credit card product which has a meaningful impact. I spoke to the Clean Energy Credit Union last week who are a non-profit and are growing. Perhaps this is the kind of product that they would embrace, if you would like an introduction.

Regarding a scoping study, Next Gen Power could potentially assist with this research. We could expand upon our Fintech mapping and create a separate more focused carveout on green banking and climate crisis credit card products (and their potential for development). As we are already studying this landscape more widely speaking, there is potential to explore this focus area on a deeper level.

I am not sure what your budget is around this scoping project but let us know if you would like to discuss this possibility further.

Thanks again for your time and insights.

Warmly,

Lewis Draper

Next Gen Power

***

Once again, Arnie and I were facing the question what's your budget? *"Lewis, we don't have a budget, but you do! We have a developed conception to create a parallel economy and a shift in the economic power structure that must happen, or our planetary life support systems are doomed. Are such conceptions a dime a dozen in your universe? Are two guys with a proven track record of incarnating a big idea to transform the organic foods world from marginal to mainstream worth a small risk of capital?"*

Given my present prime Valley location, the answer was obviously not. Perhaps Arnie and I should have sucked it up and found the money. But something didn't feel right, and I am glad we did not. We wanted a collaboration. We were ready to join with others and bust our butts to put some money together to get a feasibility study done. But we were not going to be reduced to being two entrepreneurs needing consultants and money to pay them so we could finally get into a business. That would not be us this time around. We had earnestly tried to get Woorim to join as a collaborator. We asked him/his organization to contribute $12,500 and we would do the rest to get to $100K. Dead-end. And now we were in a similar moment with Lewis and Next Gen. SO-SO.

***

#24

May 6, 2020

Hi Lewis,

Thanks for the prompt reply.

Yes, Arnie and I are interested in the scoping/feasibility study and appreciate your offer to possibly assist. The study is a necessary step. Assumptions will be tested; the tires of what we are envisioning will be kicked; essential expertise will be identified; and potential collaborators will come into focus.

Regarding a budget, our mindset is to keep things very tight. A three to four-month timeframe comes to mind as a first pass. Starting with Arnie and myself, we will engage for either no pay or a nominal amount such as a $1000 each per month. The nominal amount idea was suggested to us as a means to formally acknowledge our rolls in the project. Any compensation for us is not a budgeting concern.

We have reached out to Woorim Hindan, CEO at Akash Social Enterprise in Los Angeles. This past January he threw out to us a $100K estimate for a study. I think he had in mind engaging an attorney in his network with a lot of start-up banking experience, particularly around possible organizational structures (i.e. B-Corps, Cooperatives, Credit Units, Perpetual Trusts and Not-for-Profits) and related charters. Also, Allen Moss, past CEO and President of the ALD Trust (who Arnie and I met with along with Woorim) might have a role as consultant and would need to be budgeted for.

What is unknown to us are the potential resources within your universe at Next Gen Power or possibly at the Hewlett Foundation. Also, there may be synergies with the Clean Energy Credit Union initiative that Arnie and I would certainly like to explore.

So, let's brainstorm this possibility of a scoping/feasibility study and see how we can flesh it out together.

Arnie and I understand you have many other ongoing commitments. We are used to working independently and would expect to do so once we were all aligned with the objectives, goals and general approach of the study.

Our schedules are usually flexible. We look forward to the next zoom and the next step forward.

Best,

Ron and Arnie

***

Uh oh. 14 days of silence from Lewis.

***

#25

May 20, 2020

Hi Lewis,

Trust you are well and that the COVID situation in your immediate environs is being well-managed and moving in the right direction. Both Vermont and Hawaii seem to fortunately have committed leadership that is sensibly weighing health concerns with re-starting their respective economies. It's uncharted territory.

Arnie and I are checking-in with you regarding our May 6 follow-up communication on the scoping/feasibility study. We would like to take another step forward and would appreciate an update.

We see both a pressing need and great potential to unite consumer and commercial capital into a movement that finances climate change mitigating actions with subsequent impact. To succeed with de-carbonizing and ecological restoration at the scale needed within the pressurized timeframe confronting us all, requires exploring and investing in new approaches. It is not only investment barriers and the general flow of capital to global warming actions that need to be addressed, but the means to bring people together such that they are empowered and hopeful for a sustained period.

Best regards,

Ron Koss & Arnie Koss

***

#26

May 20, 2020

Hi Ron and Arnie,

Thanks for the kind follow up. I've spoken with Peter Neal, our Program Director about a possible scoping of the "Green Credit Card" landscape and comprehensive feasibility study. My understanding is that Next Gen Power is capable of taking on this effort if appropriate resources are sourced. From a cursory view, we estimate this effort would take 4-6 months and cost approximately $12-$15k per month.

This work would involve interviews of key stakeholders, synthesis of their advice into a report, a mapping of existing products and landscape, and initial product development with subject matter experts to create a proof of concept for a Climate Crisis Credit Card.

If you think this is a scope of work that is worth exploring to a deeper level, perhaps we should have a follow-up conversation. We agree this concept is a viable business idea if it is structured properly with the right partners.

Warmly,

Lewis Draper / Next Gen Power

***

So, *Next Gen Power* offered to join us as "hired guns." Arnie and I knew we weren't going down that one-way street. The *PARALLEL* story unfolding here is particular to Arnie and me, but it represents a much bigger story and problem for changing the world or at least the way it operates. And that is what I am talking about and what is needed – changing the world.

The phrase "changing the world" is triggering to some because it is so audacious. But I can't emphasize enough that what one deems "magical thinking" and delusional naivete may just represent a mindset and artificial boundary. Remember jet travel and computers were such impossibilities to most people 100 years ago.

Nonetheless, a collective mindset is monumental in its own right. It sets the placement of the fulcrum for this moment on Planet Earth. On one side are those representing conventional thinking and the range of expressions of protracted inertia. On the other side of the pivot point are those who have a different belief of who or what is delusional and what is possible or impossible. It is easy to imagine how our seesaw presently tilts. We all know where the fulcrum sits and where the leverage advantage lies....with convention and the ordinary.

Arnie and I knew we were surrounded by money and simultaneously constrained by its gatekeepers and access to it.

Similar stories of must-happen ideas and impulses litter the Valley.

I have no advice or sage wisdom to offer my Valley-mates. I can commiserate and that's it.

***

#27

May 31, 2020

Hi Lewis and Peter,

Arnie and I sincerely appreciate your engagement and effort to brainstorm with us to find a viable way forward and produce a potentially impactful result.

Here are some post-zoom reflections on our conversation.

First, it is indisputable that we are faltering. CO2 is rising. The globe continues to warm.

Arnie and I are not championing the Climate Emergency Credit Card idea because we think a credit card itself is the answer to the global warming problem. That reduction misses the mark.

The credit card, however, focuses us on four pillars that are essential to answering the key question – How do we build a sustainable climate IMPACT movement at scale to reduce the peril and stop the faltering?

From these four pillars emerge the support for a platform (aka paradigm) that will help create the urgency needed to prevent systemic collapse. The credit card is one of many initiatives needed that will rest upon this platform.

Four Pillars:

1) There is one stakeholder – Planet Earth. All actions pass through "her" to the benefit of "us."

2) Capital accumulation, creation and control at scale are essential.

3) Global human potential on behalf of the stakeholder must be activated and become engaged.

4) This human potential must be connected & mobilized into a transformative social/consumer movement.

Each pillar requires a deep dive. The scoping study would accomplish this by utilizing the credit card as a tangible means to ground and give context to the platform being envisioned.

Right now, the current "operating system" running our collective lives and impacting our planet has a design flaw that threatens life as we know it. One effect is that it hijacks the best ideas, focuses our human energy on ownership percentages, reduces success to an ROI calculation (triple bottom-line efforts are inconsequential to date) and moves the horizon from a visionary future to a preoccupation with exit strategies and cashing out.

Mitigating efforts that now span generations of activism, regulation and countless entrepreneurial initiatives prove the point. The design flaw confronting us is very clever. It gives us enough rope…. to hang ourselves.

Your engagement with us speaks to the fact that you also see this point.

Nonetheless, the status quo keeps trying to fix global warming with this broken operating system that should, at this point, be relegated obsolete. It is failing us all in front of our eyes.

Lewis and Peter, who is it that is supposed to be B.R.A.V.E. in the Hewlett conception?

Arnie and I need a grant to do this pioneering work and discernment. We are pre-angel. We are asking for nothing for ourselves. The money to do the scoping study represents a small investment for an exploration that we all agree is timely and needed.

Thank you for considering our input and perspective.

Best regards,

Ron and Arnie

***

#28

June 2, 2020

Ron and Arnie,

Thanks again for the collaborative discussion. While I do agree that our interests are aligned around a climate crisis credit card, unfortunately we seem to be at a bit of an impasse when it comes to project management. As much as Peter and I believe in the mission and product you are looking to explore, we have bitten off quite a bit for chewing already in our current mandates, and so in order for us to take on another project we also need to hire and direct a concerted outreach and research effort.

Some potential avenues forward which come to mind:

1) Ron and Arnie source capital for feasibility study, Next Gen Power conducts study, results and next steps are shared as deemed appropriate.

2) Ron and Arnie further develop the business plan/model (create LLC and website), Next Gen then runs the startup and helps to source capital as well as partnerships in 2021.

3) Ron and Arnie look for outside grants to fund a feasibility study, apply to RFPs, and then conduct or share the research burden per their discretion.

While this may not be exactly what you were hoping for, I do hope these suggestions are helpful. We want to see this idea developed to the level where it can create real impact.

Warmly,

Lewis Draper

Next Gen Power

***

I want to be clear. Lewis was not being unreasonable. He was trying to be helpful, but Arnie and I could not meet him. We did not have the wherewithal in that moment to go down any of his suggested roads.

We believed in order to raise angel money we needed *Next Gen Power* on board as a partner, albeit limited. We believed we needed Woorim and the Akash Social Enterprise on board as a collaborator. And the same with Josh at the Amalgamated Bank and Bill McKibben, Paul Hawken and Naomi Klein as well.

With that A+ team, Arnie and I would have ventured out into the world, to the ends of the world and found the bulk of the money we needed to do that feasibility study.

Chapter 16 - Welcome to the Valley of Death

<u>We Did our Best.</u>

<u>#29</u>

June 4, 2020

Hi Lewis and Peter,

Thanks for your prompt reply.

Arnie and I will have to think on this.

The impasse is admittedly disappointing. The "Valley of Death" that Marilyn writes about is a real place. Our effort has not arrived at that location, but we know it might.

Organic baby food, a no-brainer today, took 3 years of pounding the pavement and extracted a great sacrifice from us to get it launched. We flirted mightily with landing in that Valley. Arnie and I had to give up 40% of the company for $500K of equity. You can imagine where that starting point led to.

Today, even if an entrepreneur clears enough hurdles to get funded and survive, survival, from our viewpoint is not sufficient at this time. Surviving within a paradigm that is driving us towards ecological catastrophe offers only the illusion of success.

How do we build a sustainable climate IMPACT movement at scale to reduce the peril and stop the faltering?

Without doing the foundational work to answer this question, we are locked into the status quo and failing, in effect, to meet the global crisis. What was so refreshing in reading some of Marilyn's' writing is that she understands the centrality of this, which is why she, on her own and to our surprise, made an effort to keep our Climate Emergency Credit Card impulse alive.

Arnie and I understand that you are committed to other mandates. But what do you think about giving us an opportunity to present to Marilyn? It just seems crazy that a small amount of money, in the grand scheme of things, for such important work is standing in our way.

What allows me to be bold in continuing to push as I am is the clarity that Arnie and I are not advocating for an opportunity for ourselves. This is not about us or for us. This is about staring in the mirror, as Bill McKibben and 22 other climate activist luminaries did a year ago last April (2019) and concede that everything on the table and in motion environmentally, politically and activist-wise does not represent the urgency necessary to avert the collapse of our planetary life support systems. Their bleak declaration, not ours.

The questions Arnie and I are asking, the solutions we are envisioning and the collaborations we are hoping for are aimed at both acknowledging this sobering assessment and doing the due diligence necessary to chart a more hopeful path.

What do you think? A 15- or 30-minute zoom with Marilyn?

Thanks for considering this.

Ron and Arnie

***

#30

June 14, 2020

Lewis and Peter,

I trust you are continuing to safely manage the COVID situation.

I am re-sending our May 31 email to you.

Arnie and I remain hopeful that you are considering our proposal to have a conversation with Marilyn. We believe it's imperative to do this scoping study. It is not just particular to what we are envisioning. It is relevant to everything in the global warming sphere.

The current paradigm of action and activism is failing us. It is economic. It is cultural. It is class and race. It is political. We all know this.

With the stakes so high, there must be a solution to this $50K or $100K impasse. We are not confronted here by a scarcity problem. Rather, we are facing the persistent cascade of rationales and circumstances that has made the Valley of Death so prominent a fixture in the global warming story we are all a part of.

We look forward to your input.

Best,

Ron and Arnie

***

#31

June 16, 2021

Hi Ron and Arnie,

We are deep in our accelerator program build so apologies for a delayed response. My impression is that Marilyn is extremely busy right now, though Peter holds that relationship and can opine a bit more on the best approach.

If you have not already, perhaps there is a grant here which is worth exploring: https://hewlett.org/grants/

If you can find one which is a fit, this avenue might be viable.

Best,

Lewis Draper/ Next Gen Power

***

Pain is pain. Arnie and I had failed. I understood why, but I could not accept the explanation. The impossible cannot be impossible. How could we as a species accomplish so much, express so much beauty in its myriad ways and yet be so foolish? How could inertia be more powerful than facts, than knowing and our free will as human beings to act as stewards for the future?

***

#32

June 19,2020

Dear Lewis and Peter,

I am trying to make sense with where we have landed.

First, the suggestion that Marilyn, who recommended us to you, is too busy to engage in one of the glaring sectors (retail banking) that she recognizes has been overlooked and that we are uniquely addressing is disappointing.

This should not be the result of our shared engagement.

Who will manifest the urgency needed to prevent the collapse of our planetary life support systems that Bill McKibben and other prominent activists lament, if not for you and others like us?

Our Climate Emergency Credit Card is one such response. It is just the beginning of what is needed.

Lying latent within the needed actions to transform the access to capital that we are all aligned with is, as we envision, a worldwide consumer movement. This is what is needed to drive innovation, shape political will, and bring about necessary regulatory actions.

The Credit Card will become an important tool to support this.

The "talk" that Arnie and I have encountered on our journey is all about the deficiencies in the system and the necessity to be B.R.A.V.E. The "walk," however, stubbornly sits and fits within the comfort zone and mindset of established/traditional institutional behaviors.

One of the casualties of this ordinariness is the needed urgency we keep referring to.

Case in point is sending Arnie and me a link to the granting universe at Hewlett. Though no doubt well intended, it does not register as a response that meets the moment of the crisis, we are in.

Lewis and Peter, please engage with us further to get this scoping study in motion.

Please give us an opportunity to engage with Marilyn and her with us.

Best,

Ron and Arnie

***

The End

#33

June 29, 2020

Hi Lewis and Peter,

I understand from your last email that you are "deep in your accelerator program build."

Perhaps this accounts for the delay in your response to our last email.

In putting a "period" at the end of our exchanges, I want to close with this.

Activism-as-usual is failing. Bill McKibben acknowledges this, and he and many others are searching for a solution.

Arnie and I frame this dilemma as: If the possible is failing us, what is the impossible that would not?

Without a significant shift in the flow of capital; a re-direct of consumer dollars on behalf of de-carbonizing and ecological restoration; and the leveraging of philanthropy to address risk averse lending and investing, we will certainly continue to falter as we are.

There is plenty of understanding on the matters above, but in our estimation, not enough "grokking" (deep knowing and integration).

And it is only this grokking that can overcome the faltering of the ordinary and predictable and lead to the "audacious," "visionary" and "exponential" actions that this planet needs.

Arnie and I have tried our hardest to garner your support but have failed to advance what we believe needs to happen. This is disappointing.

Nonetheless, we will continue to do our best to move forward and appreciate your efforts at Next Gen Power.

Best regards,

Ron Koss and Arnie Koss

***

<u>#34</u>

June 29, 2020

Hi Ron,

Thanks for the follow up email. Peter and I fully support your cause, but we are unsure how to support you at this stage. We provide funding and advice to startup companies which are addressing the climate crisis. Unfortunately, the loose form of a feasibility study is not something that we or Marilyn have the ability to financially support, even if we all support the underlying philosophy.

Without a website, a business plan, and an LLC entity it becomes difficult to advocate for the concept. To oversimplify, we strongly encourage you to turn this idea into a concrete business so that we can more readily support you.

If you are set on a research effort first (a study), I do firmly believe that grant money or academic support is the arena to pursue. I don't know what this landscape looks like however, and I am sorry I can't be more specific.

We are seeing exploration of the card space by other groups, large and small, and so we believe there is viability. Please let us know once you get more shape and scope around the business and we will happily advocate for you.

Warmly,

Lewis Draper / Next Gen Power

***

I know one side of the coin can fairly criticize Arnie and myself for refusing to play by the rules and failing to turn our ideas into a concrete business as Lewis advised above. I know we could have delayed and possibly avoided seeing the "Welcome to the Valley of Death" road sign if we had invested the time and energy to find grant money. But we were not able to conform to those rules. They didn't meet our timetable. They did not reflect the urgency that was compelling us. It was an all or nothing proposition. Arnie and I were choosing nothing because we did not believe in the something approach Lewis was putting on the table.

<u>A "Big E" Blind Spot that Must be Faced</u>

I also know this. The reality that speaks of an $11 billion foundation lacking an almost homeopathic dilution of funding to do a feasibility study for a "cause that it fully supports" is held captive by an old failing paradigm that is subject to consequential blind spots. One of those "Big E" blind spots lies in the insistence that the path to accelerating the response to the global climate crisis is through the worn out plain vanilla capitalist model of forming an LLC, building a business plan, and then finding investors.

It is about time the post-mortem was written on this approach. I will volunteer to write it.

What follows in Part 3 is more of the fleshing out of the alternative *PARALLEL* paradigm that I envision and an answer to the question – If not the tried, true and failing capitalist model that boxes in entrepreneurs to having to declare "exit strategies" to attract investors before they've even launched their dream, then what?

***

<u>Last but Not Least</u>

#35

June 29, 2020

Dear Ron and Arnie,

I hope you are both doing well and am sorry for being so slow to respond to your emails. While I know that we share a passion for making change and for being the courageous change we want to see in the world, I do not have the bandwidth to focus building a climate bank at this time. One reason that I had not responded yet is that I've constantly been looking for a way to not to have to say 'great idea but I can't do it'. The idea you brought is so compelling and yet it requires significant human and financial resources. At this point though, I think your conclusion is fair – if disappointing.

ASE will continue to build out our lending and investing focused on climate and the planet, which feels to me like the way I can personally contribute most effectively to changing how this world works with money to bring healing.

Wishing you both all the best. I do hope that our paths cross again and am grateful that they did.

Woorim

PART 3
Life in the Valley

Chapter 17 – Where is Godzilla When We Need Him?

March 9, 2021

I am writing Part 3 from my Valley location. The sun shines here, but it stays low in the sky. I am daydreaming about the resurrection of my *PARALLEL* impulse. Spring and Easter are around the corner. Is that what I've been waiting for? Maybe I will catch a companion wave that will lift me out of the Valley. One can hope. I certainly have not seen any stairs or elevators out of this place, but I am always looking.

Nine COVID months have passed since email #35 from Woorim. I don't know where the time has gone. I attribute the gap to being splattered in defeat here on the Valley floor and to COVID hibernation.

I am writing again in good faith and a clear unknowing. I have nothing within me about which to proselytize. So, please do not mistake the certitudes that will probably soon follow for arrogance or naivete. Charitably, consider it chutzpah, at least for a while. I don't know what will unfold on the pages ahead because the blur in front of my minds-eye feels too big and the related images resist sharpening, so far.

I limit myself to one step at a time and faith.

Impossibility is a theme in my writing because I do not accept it. I do not accept our fate as virtual lemmings doomed to run off the climate cliff. Nor do I accept that the "othering" of people is a bitterness built into the human cake that will forever be. Nor do I accept the "money in our politics" disease that erodes the foundation of our Republic.

I believe in possibility. I do not care what has been for a thousand years or a hundred or five. The questions that persist within me are... What is failing us?... What is needed?... What must be? Then learn from what has been in order to possibly make... what must be... so.

I believe in our human potential.

I want to bring you way out on the limbs that I am discovering and exploring. There is no danger. The limbs never break for the guests perching on them. I need companions on this journey. I need help.

I want you to find or feel a toehold within the impossible realm, wherever it might be on the continuum of human challenges if not failings – not just related to global warming – and then to hopefully and determinedly find another toehold and another.

If the possible is failing us, what is the impossible that would not? This is the road we must venture down together whether it is impossible or not.

The exchanges, detailed in Part 2, that Arnie and I had with Bill McKibben, Woorim at Akash Social Enterprise, Josh at the Amalgamated Bank and Lewis at Next Gen Power in 2020 proved promising but ultimately disappointing. We could not convert Bill's flattering compliment to our "fascinating idea," nor Woorim's, "I'm in complete agreement with your diagnosis and analysis," nor Lewis's "keen interest" in our *Climate Emergency Credit Card* to a forward stride that would not wash away in the rain.

Certainly, you could attribute that miserable result to Arnie's and my shortcomings and deficiencies. Arguably, we should have found our own angels. We should have had a business plan. Better yet, we should have had a business. We should have advanced our grand ideas with more grounding. We should have been younger. We should have had a more impressive team on board.

Yes, let's give a nod to all the above "should haves." Arnie and I could have been better, but we were good and accomplished enough for *PARALLEL* to have taken a fledgling step towards its incarnation into this world.

Jumping a Lane

As I try to penetrate the why of landing in this Valley, I understand that for each encounter – Bill, Woorim, Josh and Lewis – we asked the same perceptibly impossible thing. Please bust out of your lane. Please stand outside of your silo. Please take a chance and respond to your impulses.

Certainly, Arnie and I had jumped the lane reserved for aspiring entrepreneurs. We were not looking for a personal upside, income, ownership or even control. We were not protecting any intellectual property. We were an open book trying to make the case that staying in our respective lanes is failing this planet.

But jumping a lane is arguably contrary to our human nature. First, it is unlikely that a person even realizes that they are in a lane. But it does not matter one way or the other. There is resistance. We have these constructs of belief and understanding so deeply ingrained and attached to our interior selves that reflexively cause us to maintain comfort, familiarity, and safety. You don't jump your lane unless necessary. You can look, flirt, and get tantalizingly close but you don't touch without taking a risk you might regret. Endless variations play out on this theme, but the gist is the gist.

Add the SO-SO Force to our lane jumping aversion and you have what we have – the climate cliff in clear view dead ahead.

Climate change does not present itself (yet) as an imminent personal threat. This is the bottom-line here. There is plenty of "talk" on the matter to the contrary, but in my estimation not the "walk." It doesn't matter enough that we are educated and know differently. Amazon Rainforest this, ocean acidification that, CO2 this and peat bogs and mangroves that. The first ever Colorado River shortage is now declared. All the dire related facts in the world are not yet internalized such that they evoke the fear of a gun held to the temple or those Pearl Harbor bombs or those 9-11 planes falling from the sky.

Thus, a million reasons or excuses for things to either stay the same or change, but only modest changes and within the confines allowed by any give lane, norm, or silo. This is the underlying reason why our forays with Bill, Woorim, Josh, and Lewis did not add up to a baby step forward.

Why am I so certain of this analysis? Because of these three facts and this one result. First, climate change activism is plainly faltering. Ask Bill McKibben. Two, the unraveling of our global life support systems is gaining momentum. Three, there is an hourglass that we are subject to that cannot be turned over and it is running out of sand. Those who are paying close attention realize the common knowledge of these three facts. It is not me catastrophizing. And yet no one jumped over the smallest hurdle to explore something they seemed to genuinely support. Bill, Woorim, Josh, Lewis and others I have not included in this tale of woe all stayed in their lane.

Global warming remains a crisis in name only, not of sufficient action. Buckets abound, but no brigade. Clearing two of those three feet of the collective hurdle in front of us that would save us from the clutches of Godzilla is certainly action, even admirable action – action like *Strike for the Climate*, memberships in environmental organizations, investing in solar panels, instituting the Paris Accord - but I think we can all agree, if we clear only two of those three feet to safety, we fall a little short. I am certain Godzilla would agree.

By the way, where is Godzilla when we need him to scare the bejesus out of us?

When a crisis and a threat become personal to the bone, the brain recalibrates, and synapses start reshuffling themselves. In that moment you are ready to jump your lane. In fact, you know you have to.

So, here I am. I have no plan yet. I am not sure if I ever will. I could give up. If I did, Valley management promises to buy me a coach ticket out of this place. This offer is advertised everywhere here. I am tempted because if I did let go, this burden that I feel would lift. But I guess I am not ready. What is wrong with me?

Instead, I am wondering what would *PARALLEL* be if I fleshed it out more? What would it look like if it were in this world?

Chapter 18 – Living into //

I define *PARALLEL* in its simplest expression as a climate activist driven economic paradigm that runs parallel to our current broken profit addicted capitalist system. It solely exists to re-direct consumer and commercial purchasing power towards de-carbonizing and rewilding to slow down if not reverse the global warming trend.

// is not a dictate or an "ism" nor does it require the dissolution of traditional capitalism. After all, why make things difficult? The *PARALLEL* conception aims to compete with that "ism" and prevail by winning hearts and minds in the broadest sense possible – by building the biggest tent impossible. The foundational ethos of // calls for inclusion, that is, building alliances anywhere and everywhere. Only then will it succeed.

The future we need will not manifest around a polarity such as we are the good guys and the profit seeking folks are the bad guys. Rather the future we need will manifest around reducing that polarity and expanding the understanding of how we view success and then how to achieve it. Ideally over time, the parallel realities will get closer and closer together until they appear to have merged. That will be success.

Toughness and determination also infuse the inclusive spirit of *PARALLEL*. This is not a contradiction. The // journey will not be a walk in the park. The "Welcome Mat" is not going to be out until we win the battle for hearts and minds or at least until the tide has perceptibly turned. Emphasis in this paragraph focuses on the word "battle" as in "will" – the will to find a way to build a movement to stop our collective faltering.

// will still depend on capital but rather than secure it from traditional profit seeking investors, *PARALLEL* will uniquely and creatively rely on philanthropy and borrowing. More on this in Chapter 20 – The Philanthropy Sector.

To re-emphasize, *PARALLEL* is not a "business" idea. It is a solutions-oriented paradigm. Although it will encompass many businesses, its raison d'etre is not to be a business. Money making in the ordinary sense is driving us all into a ditch. So, what's the point of doing that if you know where you are headed?

I am repeating this point in many permutations, perhaps to your annoyance, because we appear to have a thing for that ditch. Does someone know something about it that I don't know? One of my favorite lines from the movie Forest Gump comes to mind – *Stupid is as stupid does.*

As I wrote in Part 1, // has only only one shareholder – Planet Earth. Of course, we human beings will benefit profoundly because we live on the sole shareholder's property. But *PARALLEL* is not just about us. Rather it is by us for the Planet and conveniently also our very life support systems.

Given the preoccupation and mobilization around vaccinations at the time of this writing, think of // as a vaccine to prevent unbridled entropy – the tendency to disorder and separation, in other words, the tendency for our human energy to disperse, fizzle and lose its organization and cohesiveness.

PARALLEL aims to counter this dissolution or to at least moderate it. It aims to bring people together, but not just in moments of inspiring and uplifting actions and not just within their silos of activism.

The // conception intends to bring people together as both a movement without boundaries and one that requires little effort or sacrifice to participate in or join. The difference between a moment and a movement mirrors the difference between a tree and a forest of trees. Presently, there are a lot of moments of activism, a lot of trees. The fight against global warming and the failure of our planetary life support systems certainly requires these moments, these trees, but only if they are tied together into a forest ecosystem or movement to become the systemic change that we need.

Millions of trees are wonderful and beautiful, but they are not enough. We need a parallel and complementary effort to our focus on the understanding of natural systems and what makes them resilient applied to the understanding of human systems, dynamics, and behaviors. What could make our organization, as a species, capable of meeting a nemesis of its own making – global warming?

PARALLEL is that Other Way.

PARALLEL must be a from-the-bottom-up to the top global people's movement. It is evolutionary in its aim to withstand the entropy that undoes the efforts to effectively organize ourselves and overcome the inertia of our dissolution caused by greed, ignorance, and economic injustices. It is revolutionary in its aim to create something globally cohesive and imbued with an innate, self-organizing intelligence and determination.

But to be clear, *PARALLEL* does not require personal enlightenment nor economic and political revolution. It does not require a radical shift in the consciousness of humanity. *//* will re-direct exactly what is to what exactly what must be.

What is, is capitalism serving as a means for economic survival but at the expense of our planetary life support systems. What must be is also a means for economic survival but without that self-destructive price tag. *PARALLEL* is that other way. It will give people around the globe a viable way to be empowered by their purchasing power, a path, in effect, to dictate the future behavior of not only corporations but of any representative democracy, also dependent upon the will of the people.

The point is clear: people do not just buy, they also vote. Corporate profit-making will not be banished but it will have to compete with a *PARALLEL* reality determined to educate consumers and offer them as many *PARALLEL* branded choices and *PARALLEL* aligned choices as possible.

So, fear not New Confederates and those of you who are worried about a socialist take-over. The laws of the business jungle will not be re-legislated or overthrown by a progressive empire in this conception. Rather it will be the influence of a *PARALLEL* reality that will bend and re-order the values and the behaviors that are driving us down this overheated road.

You may wonder why would I ever think people are going to unite as a movement sufficient to impact corporations and government policy making and spending? That has not happened today or ever, why would it suddenly happen tomorrow?

<u>Can You Believe the Answer to this Question?</u>

For the same simple reason that sourdough starter, water, rye flour, caraway seeds, and sea salt do not make delicious sour dough rye bread until they are added in the proper proportions, mixed, rested, fermented, risen, and baked...by someone. Having all the ingredients prove necessary but obviously not sufficient for the end result. It is not like sourdough rye bread is inevitable just because the ingredients are sitting on the kitchen counter. But it is possible.

Moments similarly are necessary ingredients but not sufficient in themselves to create a movement with enough clout and resilience to change the trajectory of our warming globe. However, with both the ingredients and intention in place, a // reality is also possible.

This rye bread analogy underlies my thinking about *PARALLEL*. We have the ingredients for the movement (or loaf) I am writing about in place. There are tens if not hundreds of millions of people world-wide concerned about climate change right now and billions more potentially waiting in the wings. There is an aligned scientific community and a vibrant and growing activist community. International youth organizations are flourishing. Corporations are always looking for the next frontier and will follow like a puppy if there is food/opportunity in front of it. And there is tremendous philanthropic wealth in place accompanied by its potential to catalyze the changes that inspired it.

I am not trying to identify every ingredient above or detail the process to bring everything together. I am not writing the // manual. I am trying to convey a conception of *PARALLEL* – what I am aiming for and why it is possible. This is what I am hoping you will grok.

PARALLEL is the *BAKER* entrepreneur in this stream of consciousness. It intends to be the underlying intelligence that recognizes the necessary ingredients that are already in place; identifies and secures what others might be needed; and then skillfully, collaboratively, and willfully charts a course to mix and process them into a "loaf" or a movement.

Moment-makers, organizations like 350.org, Green Peace and NRDC, have been doing the hard work of climate crisis education and battling on behalf of the environment for decades. They have been ceaselessly striving to transform their efforts into the necessary impact that would be sufficient to protect our planetary life support systems.

Despite the dire April 3, 2019 open letter in the British daily newspaper, The Guardian, that alarmed me so, the efforts and actions of these moment-makers have manifested many of the "ingredients" necessary for the // movement being fleshed out in these pages to emerge. You don't have a movement without these moments.

PARALLEL provides the synergy and neural network that is missing. It does not substitute for all the actions that are in motion. It does not compete for membership or funding with established organizations. Rather, it allies and advocates. In fact, when established // will become a funder and a lender. *PARALLEL* aims to do only what is necessary.

In my estimation what is necessary requires a quickening and unifying force, an unwavering global constant that will connect the myriad of dots, those precious moments of actions and initiatives, and potentize them into a movement.

This movement is the impossible that will not fail us.

// Kool-Aid

I am not channeling Pollyanna. I am not envisioning a "changed" world in any absolute sense. Our present, non-*PARALLEL* reality will not magically disappear. Everyone is not going to drink the // Kool-Aid. There still will be an us and a them. There will still be New Confederates, climate change deniers, bad-actor corporations, waste, and economic injustice. But there will be markedly less of that, and the balance of power will start to tip in the // direction.

Why? Because the connected dots will present themselves as a tangible and dynamic choice that does not feel diffuse and ephemeral. They will present themselves as that BIG tent with many portals of entry. The opportunity to be a part of something empowering and hopeful will be plain to see.

The ease of participating and the accompanying gravitas of // as a game-changer will attract people as they perceive what is possible. The global yearning for solutions to the climate crisis expands as each global event hits home. The readiness for *PARALLEL* grows every day. A // free market economy united by a singular focus – global warming – lies within our reach.

Remember, five steps forward and two back is okay.

Momentum promises to grow exponentially as the first // toeholds appear. Moments of action will integrate more and more into the *PARALLEL* movement. A // reality will become our norm and the era we are in will recede into the past and become known to those in the future as the *Age of the Near Miss* – the time when we mistook freedom for license. The time when we thought that "or" was the conjunction between living free and dying as in "Live Free or Die" rather than "and" as in "Live Free and Die." The time when we fiddled while our planet burned. The time when the bucket brigade showed up at the last minute. Nearly a disaster – A Near Miss.

In our *PARALLEL* life, a united global climate activist consumers' movement will dictate, in the relative near term, corporate priorities and actions. The Law of the Jungle says so. Capitalist behaviors must either serve the wishes of those who feed it, or perish.

And it must be in the "relative near term!"

Chapter 19 – The First Toehold

We Become the Powerful by Giving that Possibility a Chance.

Remember, I am writing from the Valley of Death. For all my talk of "readiness growing every day," I was unable to convince those already aligned with my sentiments and alarm to take a supporting step forward with me. What gives me any sense of optimism given my location?

Experience.

When you believe you are onto something important, you don't give up. What if failure makes you better? What if failure is a prelude to success? I admit my connection to this ethos is weak right now, but I guess it fits like an old shoe and a place toward which I naturally default.

The incarnation of *PARALLEL* will take a village. I know this. I am not writing with all the answers or know-how in tow. I recognize that I lack much of the expertise needed. I also recognize that I am holding and trying to capture a unique vision. I believe this is a strength of mine and important and what I can contribute.

You may recall that Bill McKibben wrote in FALTER that "we have the tools to stand up to the powerful and reckless." And my response was and remains – *PARALLEL* sets out with an additional objective – to become the powerful. This is the only way. But how do we do that?

We become the powerful by giving that possibility a chance. It is that simple, and so far we have not done that adequately.

PARALLEL will Start with a Pool of Several Billion Dollars.

In Part 1, I wrote about the // Bank, // Lending and the // *Climate Emergency Credit Card*. These represent the first toeholds in building the *PARALLEL* conception.

The 30,000' view looks something like this. The // Bank will underwrite a credit card – the PARALLEL Climate Emergency Card and offer a lending program, PARALLEL Lending, dedicated to its one stakeholder. It will have a charitable giving arm, PARALLEL Giving, that provides grants to decarbonizing and restoration initiatives. Strategically, // will innovate lending to entrepreneurial initiatives by leveraging philanthropic dollars to mitigate risk. An alternative to Amazon might be one such initiative.

Maybe this starting point takes too big of a bite. Maybe. But on the other hand, maybe the reticence I just expressed concerning the size of the bite gives voice to conventional thinking, or (my) senior age, or the wisdom gleaned from and relevant to an ordinary entrepreneurial life but not to a global crisis navigating the fastest route possible, according to my GPS, to calamity.

Maybe there is an alternative way to work collaboratively with the Akash Social Enterprise, the Amalgamated Bank, the ESG (Environmental, Social, Corporate Governance) universe or within the Credit Union and Cooperative corner of the financial world? I am looking for the beeline to results. I am not attached to the means, but rather the ends.

On paper, collaboration would be ideal. If we could avoid reinventing the wheel, avoid it. But I am not optimistic. I think established institutions will shy away from *PARALLEL*. The dots are too far apart. The ideas are too big and unwieldy. The not-for-profit conception casts a huge shadow on coming up with a viable capitalization strategy.

In my mind's eye I can hear the refrain from another movie, the 1989 Kevin Costner movie, Field of Dreams – *Build it and they will come*. I think this is true of *PARALLEL*. Something must be built that captures the possibility I am envisioning in real time and real life. And then they will come.

Where does the capital come from to start a bank, a lending program, and a credit card, including the growing universe of contactless transactions? Not in the ordinary way.

PARALLEL will start with a pool of several billion dollars sourced from philanthropic contributions. This money will come together as a result of satisfying three conditions.

A knock-your-socks-off management core hovering for the opportunity of a lifetime.

Buy-in from the inner circle of climate change activists like Bill.

Hollywood and/or celebrity engagement and endorsement.

Impossible, I know. But a voice within me or outside of me asks.... Why impossible?

The knock-your-socks-off management core is out there. It doesn't have to be invented. The expertise is ready. Who could disagree with that? So, that's not impossible - ☑.

Arnie and I were arguably somewhat close to buy-in from Bill McKibben. He acknowledged that we had a "fantastic idea." We also caught the attention of Marilyn Waite at the Hewlett Foundation, although she remained at arm's length. Woorim at Akash Social Enterprise may have had the strongest connection to our impulse and perhaps was closest to joining with us. Obviously, we did not succeed but I am making the case here that we showed that the needed buy-in is possible - ☑.

Celebrity engagement is an established universe. Who could disagree with that? From Jerry Lewis who raised almost $2.5 billion for the Muscular Dystrophy Association over the years to Oprah Winfrey's high-profile influence and charitable clout to global music extravaganzas such as the Concert for Bangladesh and athletic charitable events like the London Marathon that raised over $90 million in 2019, celebrity engagement on a massive global scale for climate action is just a matter of time. What this level of engagement awaits is the *PARALLEL* economic paradigm coming to light in these pages to engage its focus and rally around - ☑.

So, we don't have an impossible problem. Let's put that notion to rest.

We also can put to rest the statement *"PARALLEL will start with several billion dollars"* which I posited not because it has to be the starting point. Not at all. But maybe that kind of capitalization should be the starting point. And if so, take my point that it is not impossible, and we should be open to it.

<u>Brain-Dead Sloths</u>

If we don't open ourselves up to a new era of flexible thinking now which responds to the appropriate amount of urgency we face, then climate change will continue as the human story of the future. And we will be the brain-dead sloths that no one in that future will understand because our choices and degree of failure will be incomprehensible to them. This is very possible.

It is important to understand that these *PARALLEL* ideas are not meeting the world with a "holier than thou" chip on their shoulder. I may have disdain for the pollution caused by the burning of coal, but not for the coal miners or the millions of people doing their best to cook and stay warm.

There is not a "you" and "me" kind of divide in this global warming crisis. Yes, there are climate deniers and evil doers. Yes, there are profound and consequential economic injustices that must be addressed. Yet in the grand scheme of almost 8 billion people living their lives here on the planet surface, it boils down to only "we."

As one of those 8 billion, I have an oil furnace and a wood stove in my home. I am not above it all. I both represent the problem and want to be part of the solution. To do this, I need help. I believe this *PARALLEL* conception signifies an important piece of that help which is why I am trying to materialize and champion it here from the Valley of Death despite all odds.

//'s underlying ethos has to be to invite everyone to be a part of the solution. This is not a business strategy, but a survival response. It is the way to act when the only house on the planet – our house - is on fire.

Something else should be factored into the impossibility equation. A // Bank, lending program, and credit card are actually homerun business ideas to any open-minded, discerning pair of eyes. And by design and purpose, its profits will solely benefit climate action. Aren't there enough of us weary of the plunder of Wall Street and the other global exchanges ravaging Planet Earth? Aren't there enough of us sitting on the sidelines feeling hopeless, powerless, cynical, ambivalent, and checked-out on the subject?

PARALLEL opens a door that has been invisible: a door connecting to a movement meeting an impending crisis, a door that does not require yet another donation or membership. Most of us use credit cards and/or contactless transaction services. We also use banks. Many of us need to borrow. Why not do it all safely and securely within a *PARALLEL* world with its climate focus and dedication? Is this an impossible concept and solution? It shouldn't be.

Chapter 20 – A Philanthropy Sector

I suggested above utilizing a pool of several billion dollars derived from philanthropy to create a toehold to get *PARALLEL* started.

I believe, so far, that this approach must be the way. Terms such as investing, ownership, return on investment and exit strategies fall away in this *PARALLEL* visioning. Even B Corps, albeit with their many admirable socially responsible principles, are subject to the distractions and side-shows caused by the profit-making motive.

Not-for-profits are also subject to being compromised and diminished. Some CEOs make in excess of $1 million. The "slippery slope virus" exists within each of us and hence potentially in all human endeavor. But if we are taking bets, I will bet on the not-for-profit or possibly the cooperative economic model for a *PARALLEL* life.

Remember, I am not pouring cement. I am throwing out thoughts and leanings. Maybe the B Corp model is, at the end of the day, perfect.

Imagine a philanthropy sector that becomes centrally causal in the manifestation of a // economy. I am not suggesting that philanthropy become the singular fuel for *PARALLEL*. That would be foolish. Rather, I am imagining that philanthropy could be used to "prime the pump" to get something started. A case in point would be the feasibility study for the *Climate Emergency Credit Card* that stalled because it couldn't get funded and left me splattered here in the Valley.

Philanthropy could function both as a source of high-risk capital or it could be leveraged to make higher risk lending more viable by serving to relieve the perceived risks that cause traditional lenders to turn down prospective borrowers.

I see philanthropy and low interest lending as the bridge to self-sustaining cash flow in a *PARALLEL* world. Also, philanthropy would be the power behind aspirational "can and must-dos" when convention cannot rise above "can't do."

There is nothing revolutionary or magical in this thinking. Marilyn Waite, the Program Officer in Environment at Hewlett reflects in her writing that there is a funding problem for innovative ideas because of the conservative nature of bank lending and the difficulties of attracting investment capital to high-risk entrepreneurial initiatives. The place called the Valley of Death, otherwise known to me as the business graveyard, is a term that Marilyn has used and one I can obviously relate to.

Philanthropy is a frontier that is not far out on Cloud 9. It is right in front of us, and we need to creatively parlay it right now with abandon. Serving as a risk mediator, philanthropy will underlie the delivery of a // choice and its transformative potential to meet the global warming crisis.

Americans donated almost $450 billion in 2019 (The Conversation, June 16, 2020, Anna Pruitt). Corporate giving reached $21 billion, and foundations contributed about $76 billion – almost $550 billion in total. In Europe, 90 billion euros (European Economic and Social Committee, May 29, 2019) or approximately $107 billion USD was identified to be philanthropic giving.

In addition to traditional philanthropy, there is simply a lot of money floating around that could be applied to incarnating a grand idea such as a competitive *PARALLEL* economic reality. Michael Bloomberg spent around a $1 billion on his 2020 presidential campaign aspirations. Tom Steyer spent approximately $250 million on his 2020 campaign. This is the tip of the iceberg (potentially) of available brute cash to break down barriers, open doors, prove concepts, and realize *PARALLEL,* if there was only a way to mobilize that potential.

And there is a way, and it does not have to take forever until the point of no return. Why not in a twinkling of an eye?

The Metaphorical "Room" and the "Big Boat"

Why not bring together, in a metaphorical room, the powerful, the influencers, the moneyed, the connected, the communicators, and the inspirers who currently make a difference yet want to do more because they recognize the need? Bring together people like Bill McKibben, Paul Hawken, Greta Thunberg, Naomi Klein, Al Gore, John Kerry, Barack Obama, Gina McCarthy, Marilyn Waite, Oprah Winfrey, Bill Gates, Lady Gaga, Tom Steyer, Lebron James, Michael Bloomberg, Meryl Streep, Ted Turner, Warren Buffet, Andrew Yang, Robert Redford, MacKenzie Scott, Taylor Swift, Laurene Powell Jobs, Amanda Gorman, Lionel Messi, Alice Louise Walton and on and on.

The list of potential people in this metaphorical global room, prominent or not, could fill a book. Why isn't this possible? And imagine what could be realized with this kind of convergence of human energy, achievement, and consciousness! Even *PARALLEL*!!!

But how naïve of me to envision this convergence when probably nearly everyone that I have assembled in that room has bought into and financially depends on that for-profit paradigm I am intending *PARALLEL* to disrupt. Is this the catch-22 ambush that has been waiting for me?

If so.

The End.

***

But I don't think so.

The *PARALLEL* conception I am envisioning is not monolithic. Everything does not need to become //. *PARALLEL* does not take over the world nor does it have to in order to change the world. But I do think it has to pose, at least initially, as a looming presence to get the "big boat's" (our capitalist juggernaut) attention and turn it.

Establishing this presence is accomplished by the movement that *PARALLEL* will mobilize. This movement represents a meaningful slice of the marketplace that possesses disposable income. The resulting market trends represent waves, currents and winds that will get the "big boat's" attention. The bigger the // movement the bigger the waves, currents, and winds.

PARALLEL needs to become a significant and influential force. That force will inspire other entrepreneurs to align with the // ethos and become allied with the spirit of its decarbonizing and re-wilding focus. Part of the job of *PARALLEL*'s leadership is to facilitate those alliances. In this way there is plenty of room under the // tent for for-profit enterprises.

Similarly, the *PARALLEL* movement will also influence the choices and behaviors of the established and largely self-absorbed capitalist economy. Imagine if the large fast-food corporations helped reverse the deforestation of the Amazon. What a story that would be! What a win! Imagine if these same corporations wielded their influence to demand a climate responsible and cruelty-free paradigm for raising animals.

Well, maybe if *McPARALLELS* gets started tomorrow with an extraordinary amount of buzz and grabs some meaningful market share because a movement stands behind it, the above would begin to happen in response.

And // would promote these alliances. The capitalist juggernaut would begin to morph in the *PARALLEL* direction.

<u>Do We Need a Time Machine?</u>

The point is the Catch-22 does not exist. Once the "big boat" truly starts turning in the direction of de-carbonizing and re-wilding, it will not return to its old ways without a counter *PARALLEL* force. And I believe that is impossible!

Do we need a time machine that brings us all to 2050 where we learn of hundreds of millions displaced, hundreds of thousands of people dead every year from climate related disruption, coastal devastation, a weakened Gulf Stream current turning our climate lives on the east coast of North America and Western Europe upside down? You get the drift.

If we all got that grand futuristic tour of the calamity first-hand and could then transport ourselves back to today, would that metaphorical room remain a pipe dream? Would there still be disempowered, chickens with their heads cut-off laments like.... "*Where will the money ever come from? It is too risky.*" Would *PARALLEL* become a no-brainer and an imperative?

I believe, yes. And if not the *PARALLEL* ideas I am trying to capture here, then something else that meets the global warming crisis with the impact needed to stop our faltering.

Chapter 21 – // *CLIMATE EMERGENCY CREDIT CARD*

Land of Giants

The credit card world represents a complex landscape dominated by large banks like Citigroup and JP Morgan Chase and major Credit Card Networks like VISA, Mastercard, Discover and American Express.

The scale is huge in every direction that you look. It is a land of giants.

There were 45 billion U.S. card transactions in 2019 amounting to almost $4 trillion dollars (Creditcards.com, Market Share Statistics, June 17, 2021).

Credit card debt at the end of 2020 was $976 billion.

The VISA network is the largest with 336 million U.S. cardholders and 800 million worldwide.

The Mastercard network has 231 million cardholders in the U.S. and 709 million beyond.

Bank-wise, Citigroup ranks on top with 95.4 million cardholders, a 17% market share.

JP Morgan Case follows with 82.8 million cardholders representing 14.84% of the market (ValuePenguin, Largest U.S. Credit Card Issuers: 2017 Market Share Report, Yowana Wamala)

This scale demonstrates exactly why it is and is not the perfect place for *PARALLEL* to find a toehold to launch.

It is because credit cards are not an original idea. Most everyone (in developed countries) has at least one. And virtually every merchant accepts them. We find a ready super-highway of know-how and technologies in place to handle all the interfaces between banks and merchants with relative ease. In short, there is no pioneering. There is something instant for // to plug into that does not have to be created. This is potentially a big plus.

It is not the perfect place to start because banks do not materialize out of thin air nor do millions of cardholders magically hold your special card. There is inarguably a chasm between the // idea and the many demanding financial realities and unavoidable practicalities.

But that does not suggest a chasm between the // idea itself and the "ingredients" needed to bring it into the world. We have already covered this ground. The many millions of potential card-holders aligned with the *PARALLEL* ethos are already in place. They are waiting for *PARALLEL* but don't know it. The philanthropic-oriented money needed to create the *PARALLEL* Bank also stands ready and waiting for the // conception to make itself visible. *PARALLEL* is both so far away from manifesting because it is just a figment of my imagination and so close because the readiness for a // economy is screaming for a chance to be in this world and express itself.

Here is my Pitch for the *PARALLEL Climate Emergency Credit Card.*

Chapter 22 – The Pitch

If you have one iota of concern or interest about global warming, keep reading.

Apply for the *// Climate Emergency Card.* You use it like any other card with one major difference.

The // Card is backed by the not-for-profit *PARALLEL* Bank which dedicates itself solely to rewilding and decarbonizing and meeting the global warming crisis.

No other bank or credit card in the world does this.

PARALLEL needs you. Climate activism needs you. Our planetary life support systems need you.

No gimmicks. We play by a few simple rules.

Rule #1:

Your *// Climate Emergency Credit Card* will direct all the profits it earns to work with and support environmental organizations, climate scientists, activists, entrepreneurial climate-centric initiatives, educators and thought leaders, researchers, and allied media from around the globe.

Rule #2:

We mean business for the climate. Where and when necessary, your // Card will lead to create any needed initiatives to fulfill its re-wilding and decarbonizing mission. We are not reckless, or cavalier about risk-taking. But we need to take them. The global warming clock is ticking.

Rule #3:

Your // Card is transparent in its operation. No secrets. We aim to win your understanding and trust.

Rule #4:

// is a charitable 501.c3 in its official not-for-profit mission, but it is not asking you for charity. Our Climate Card wants to win your business by giving you far more of what you want than other cards do.

What do you "really" want?

Convention says you want rewards – cash back – airline miles, etc.

Agreed. We think you want rewards. Who doesn't? But we believe you want something bigger, something that has never been tested in a focus group.

We think you want more sanity in this world.

We think you want more justice.

We think you want to make a difference.

We think you want to believe something like *PARALLEL* could be for real.

We think you want to be part of the climate crisis solution...if there was only a practical way.

And there is one – a way to integrate practicality, rewards, and a change the world mission.

Consider the // Card. It will give you:

An annual card charge of $0 to $infinity. Do what you can.

Interest rate charges on any outstanding debt at 33% less than traditional charge cards.

Standard fees for cash advances, balance transfers and late fees also at 33% less.

Discounts at participating *PARALLEL* merchants whenever you use the // Card.*

Pride to be a part of a global movement that is championing a response to the climate crisis.

But how?

How can // offer you lower interests and fees than the big companies? Simple, *PARALLEL* is not building stadiums with our name on it. We have no shareholders expecting profits. We are not paying million-dollar salaries to anyone. We will not be situated in lavish office buildings. We are not spending big bucks on advertising campaigns to win you over.

And in addition to the above reasons – we are compelled to find a way. Business-as-usual is unable to meet the climate crisis. We need a // reality to lead the way and prove that the impossible is actually possible.

* <u>*PARALLEL* Rewards</u>

// will create a merchant's discount program better than your typical 2% or 3% cash back card offers. No other card can do this because, with few exceptions, no other card has a "reason-to-be" besides benefitting itself.

PARALLEL will attract millions of businesses that are allied with our cause and want to attract customers such as yourself by offering a discount to you on all // Card purchases.

The // Merchant's Program will take some time to build, but 5% - 10% discounts are possible.

Start with us. Stick with us. Help build the *PARALLEL* movement.

<u>// Pay</u>

// Pay will be a Venmo-type alternative backed by the not-for-profit *PARALLEL* Bank. It will allow you to purchase items, split checks, rent payments etc. without using a credit card.

Contactless transactions linked to your // *Climate Emergency Credit Card* are also possible. Like Venmo, // Pay services will be free except for a 3% charge for // Credit Card transactions.

Don't forget // Rule #1. All profits go towards re-wilding and de-carbonizing.

Stay tuned to learn more about <u>// Pay</u>.

<u>Finally</u>

Traditional forms of climate activism are critically needed, but they also prove not to be enough. None have challenged the for-profit economy that simply cannot help itself from being about itself.

PARALLEL is a parallel economic reality dedicated to fighting climate change that competes with but aims, as a goal, to creatively ally with its competition. Sounds like a contradiction.

Yes, but this is the challenge of building the biggest "For-the-Climate" tent possible. Everyone is a potential ally.

PARALLEL is a grand idea. But big ideas are the only ones that can tackle the climate crisis.

What ultimately makes // big is you – your buy-in and commitment to believing that you and hundreds of millions like you are ready to be united into a game-changing movement with a single purpose.

To create an alternative happy or happier ending to "The Global Warming Story."

Chapter 23 – More on the parallel *PARALLEL* Paradigm

There are many directions to explore in considering the parallel *PARALLEL* paradigm. No doubt there are low hanging fruit choices that strategically make good business sense and will accelerate the // movement. However, I am not ready to introduce that degree of granularity here.

Right now, I am imagining big and painting in broad brush strokes of possibility.

// a-zon

One intriguing parallel road to venture down centers around Amazon. This monolithic super-company is daunting to even approach. It is such a ubiquitous force in our collective sphere for better and for worse. What I am certain of is that Amazon cannot go untouched by //. There must be a parallel choice to challenge some of Amazon's ubiquity.

What could that possibly look like? What is *PARALLEL's* first move? Does it venture into the realm of cloud computing where Amazon has made massive investments and is burrowed deep, deep in our global digital infrastructure/architecture. Does it set its sights on developing a // to Whole Foods Market? Does *PARALLEL* make its mark in the consumer marketplace?

What vulnerability can be found in this trillion-dollar empire that has been developing for the last 25 years? I am not sure. Since I am most familiar with the consumer marketplace, I am naturally pulled in that direction. But remember, I'm not pouring cement.

Setting aside the above vulnerabilities question, what I'm clear on is that the *PARALLEL* conception of Amazon does not mean becoming just an Amazon twin with a different focus – re-wilding and decarbonizing. Any singular obsession, whether it be noble quests like tackling global warming or profit-making to enrich shareholders can be misguided and the cause of damaging unintended consequences.

A // a-zon that would ignore its impact on Main Street USA, that would squeeze municipalities dry to get tax advantages, that opportunistically cherry picks and destroys competitors with its own branding, that creates pace-of-work pressures on its employees causing burn-out, all in service to its singular focus would miss my point of its coming into being.

Simply switching out profit-making for re-wilding and decarbonizing would not reflect the change in consciousness that *PARALLEL* must demand of itself and then emulate as a model.

As such, I foresee a network of independent businesses united in their sharing of ecological and social justice values and utilizing the // Marketplace platform for the greatest climate activism impact possible. Challenging? Yes. Impossible? No.

PARALLEL will compete successfully with Amazon wherever and however it decides to jump into the fray for several reasons.

Consumers will respond to //'s climate change mission by supporting the // Marketplace.

Merchants will appreciate *PARALLEL's* non-compete policy on behalf of their success.

Everyone will like the win-win-win // Discount Program.

PARALLEL will deliver service, convenience, choices, and reliability in its own unique, game-changing way. People do not shop Amazon because they love enriching Jeff Bezos or Amazon's gorilla bullying tactics.

Of course, I am impatient to know more of the specifics and share them with you. But I am offering a sketch here and not a blueprint.

The only consolation, at the moment, is that I am framing the questions and capturing the conception and some ideas. And this is a start. If you could teleport yourself right now to the Valley of Death, you would see that I am standing in front of a doorway that has a sign attached to it that says in big bold red letters "STOP – THERE IS NO DOORWAY HERE." I know this is a lie. I know *PARALLEL* lives behind it. And I think within that knowing lies // a-zon.

McPARALLELS

I mentioned this idea earlier. And please, don't get thrown off by the name. In the Valley of Death, you have to entertain yourself; otherwise it is a dull existence.

Imagine a vegan, vegetarian and meat "easy-choice" place with a climate friendly focus that champions regenerative agriculture, carbon sequestration, fair trade purchasing, Amazon Rainforest and Great Northern Forest protection and so on. It would be a melting pot of food, eating philosophies, local and regional agriculture production, cultural and ethnic diversity, climate activism, the arts, music and who knows what else?

And of course, a discount offered when using the // *Climate Emergency Credit Card.*

Supporting Mc//s.... maybe I should call it the Me//ting Pot.... Anyway, simultaneously imagine a parallel to the institutional food distribution system dominated by the likes of US Foods, United Naturals, KEHE, and Sysco. Let's call it for ease *PARALLEL* FOOD SERVICE.

// FOOD SERVICE would distribute to Mc//s and, of course, as far and wide as possible in the institutional food realm. It would aim to challenge the dominance of players like United Naturals and KEHE in the natural foods world. There is an incredible business opportunity here, which means an incredible opportunity for funding climate activism. All that is needed is a well-capitalized challenger like // who lives for very different reasons than these established behemoths do.

Obviously, these BIG ideas do not just magically appear, but it also does not take magic for them to do so. It takes the money, the ethos, the know-how, the leadership, the execution and perhaps most importantly the readiness in the world-at-large.

I am writing as confidently as I am because I believe the "readiness" is in place. // FOOD SERVICE is sitting in the ether waiting for its moment. The moment is defined by you and me, us, and millions more coming together as a movement tired of feeling disempowered, tired of waiting for political ineptitude to stop, tired of the narrowness of corporate profit-making, and tired of waiting for financial institutions to grow a spine and take more risks because if not now, than when.

Enough is enough.

Also, waiting in the ether is the *PARALLEL C*limate *A*ction *F*ood *E*'mporium, the retail and pioneering // CAFÉ.

THE PARALLEL CAFÉ

First, this could be tricky territory because the aim of *PARALLEL* is not to hurt food cooperatives and smaller stores. And // FOOD SERVICE wants to become their go-to wholesale foods distributor. So, creating a retail // supermarket-type outlet might be problematic if it were a competitor. But I think there is a way.

That way involves careful targeting of the location of // CAFÉ outlets such that they compete with mainstream supermarket chains and Whole Foods Market stores but not smaller community co-ops or mom & pop outlets.

Second to note is consideration of the word "compete." Again, the point of the *PARALLEL* paradigm I am trying to bring to light is not to create a parallel twin that looks much like a Safeway, Publix, or Whole Foods. This would be failure.

In addition to its re-wilding and decarbonizing raison d'etre, imagine // CAFÉ as an innovative retail foods concept built around reducing the need for packaging and plastics and introducing the next generation of bulk foods dispensing, convenience, and resulting advantageous consumer pricing.

// CAFÉ also re-introduces the idea of community volunteer labor (in exchange for a food discount), a foundation of the early food cooperative impulse. There are good reasons why the implementation of this impulse fell out of favor and good reasons to problem solve around those reasons and build a win-win economic model for volunteers and the CAFÉ operation.

And there is more. The // CAFÉ concept will revolutionize onsite glass and stainless container washing, sanitizing, and re-use. This will require a change in behaviors and expectations from consumers and as such will cater at the outset to early adapters. Not everyone will be ready for new ways to purchase foods, but this pioneering is necessary. In a deliberate iterative process, the // CAFÉ will change the face of retail food purchasing and reduce the size and impact of its environmental footprint...forever.

Remember, 5 steps forward and 2 back will change our world. The question we need to keep asking ourselves is.... How do we do that?

Two Dynamic Food Concepts

To bring to the // CAFÉ a much bigger audience than just the early adapter cohorts, two dynamic food concept magnets will be introduced. One is an actual café I am calling the *Café Eatery* with a revolutionary seating system designed for air circulation/purification, comfort, social distancing and, looking ahead optimistically to post-COVID times, just plain old privacy.

The *Eatery* will feature street food appetizers from around the world and global traditional baked goods and classic ethnic desserts. And, of course, a universe of teas, coffees, fresh juices, shakes, etc.

Speaking of universe, the second food concept magnet that will be housed inside the // CAFÉ is what Arnie and I have been envisioning for a decade and calling the *Ice Cream Universe*. Finally, it is finding its proper home within the *PARALLEL* paradigm and inside the // CAFÉ.

The *Ice Cream Universe* brings together traditional and not so traditional frozen desserts from around the world, ranging from no churn Indian Cardamon Kulfi to Italian Gelato to Japanese Mochi to Iranian Faloodeh to Turkish Dondurma to Israeli Halva Ice Cream.... You get the idea. A universe of possibilities offer themselves: dairy and non-dairy, on sticks, in cones of every kind, cups, sandwiches and who knows what else once this gets going. And all made in small-batches right in the // CAFÉ's ice cream central mini-factory.

To point out the obvious, the theme lying within these two food magnet ideas is the globe and inclusiveness. And this is what // is all about – a globe in crisis needs a globe in action. Also, to move beyond moments of action and build a movement, inclusiveness in every way possible needs to be cultivated. There are so many reasons for "separation" between us to prevail. Nationality, race, religion, ethnicity, social class, economic status, sexual orientation, political affiliations, right-to-choose and gun control have all taken center stage to do the job. And sadly, sometimes separation may be unavoidable.

Many New Confederates scoff at the very idea of human-caused climate change. I profoundly disagree with them and will oppose them in every peaceful way possible. But I will not demonize them. Some of these people will love the *Ice Cream Universe* or the *Café Eatery* setting and its Stuffed Peruvian Empanadas or the Gata zesty Armenian pastries. The point is a // reality welcomes everyone regardless of their alignment and engagement with the global warming crisis.

Finally, for now, I imagine one more dynamic component to the PARALLEL CAFÉ concept. I am calling it *PARALLEL*× or //×. The idea plays off the symbol for prescriptions - ℞.

//× is a natural pharmacy/apothecary outlet that will live inside the CAFÉ store much like the *Ice Cream Universe* and the *Café Eatery*. It brings together, in an in-depth and responsible way, the universe of alternative medicine choices via products, expertise, information, and education. In considering this offering there are many questions to answer such as... Does //× offer a compounding pharmacy service? Does //× rent office space to licensed practitioners?

Conceptually and clearly, //× is needed and in my view is another business idea homerun if well executed. We, as consumers, are constantly trying to navigate the medical and health services world. Alternative and natural products and modalities can be confusing. They can be rife with misplaced zealotry, misinformation, and marketing sizzle. The net result shows it is often overwhelming. Money is wasted and results are poor.

//× aims to fill this void and cure this overwhelm by offering a comprehensive/enlightened product mix and services complemented by staffing expertise and related educational programs.

Of course, many stores sell supplements, herbal tinctures, and the like. //× will take it to the next level and beyond, something I know from personal experience is needed and that I can be a part of creating.

Chapter 24 – You Get the Idea

Banking, credit cards, online shopping, wholesale food distribution, restaurants, retail food sales and related complementary concepts just begin to build a *PARALLEL* paradigm.

// Media lives somewhere in the queue. Possibly // Travel? // Insurance? A *PARALLEL* version of Airbnb?

You get the idea. The challenge along the way is to remember that *PARALLEL* is not about *PARALLEL*. It does not exist for itself so it can look in the mirror and say, "Look at it me! I'm big. I am powerful." No.

Rather, *PARALLEL* is about empowering, uniting and building a movement that shifts the way we grow, consume, travel, build, landscape, heat, power, recycle and restore. Its focus is near term and long term. Everything with a carbon footprint is a target of consideration.

Every ecosystem, whether it be grasslands, mangroves, marshes, oceans, forestland, etc. that has been undone, is undermined, or under threat is a focus of the *"Game-Changer"* agreement and global plan of action.

Remember, and as I wrote earlier, *"Game-Changer" represents the web of life mapped across the globe and framed as crisis areas needing re-wilding. The priorities within each key area are identified and the action plans down to the last detail are specified to assure maximum results. "Game-Changer" is the brains behind the brute cash brawn.*

Without this in-depth continuity and understanding, you have a piecemeal quilt...a little of this, a little of that. You have silos and competition for scarce resources. The big picture stays illusive and the obstacles to establish a united and coordinated climate activist movement stay formidable.

All my // imaginings happening here in the Valley of Death are more than just a tantrum of ideas. They are remedies of consequence. I have been weaving a fabric of vertically integrated solutions starting with a foundational funding philosophy and strategy. Dependent on that philosophy is a wealth of entrepreneurial initiatives all with their own // twist.

These are Not Normal Times.

The point of it all is to consume more smartly, to usurp power from those who cannot see beyond their own self-interest and/or to re-orient their priorities and related decision-making despite themselves, to become a global political force, to materialize a transformative scale of brute cash, and to be an organizing beacon (*Game-Changer*) to direct that cash on behalf of achieving the greatest re-wilding and de-carbonizing impacts possible.

If we look at this *PARALLEL* conception in the normal way with our regular thinking caps on, it is too big, way too big. But these are not normal times. We are not facing a normal situation.

In fact, we need a mobilization with an urgency behind it like never before. I am trying to capture both the letter and the spirit of a way to meet that urgency. I have called it *PARALLEL*.

The question now is, is there a way out of this Valley for me? And to what end?

Within me lies this contradiction. I write about *PARALLEL* confidently. I believe in it. I see it as if it were in the Star Trek transporter room materializing. But is it? This is the conundrum. I am in the Valley for a reason. I failed. How could it be materializing. Am I suffering from VDS – Valley Dreaming Syndrome? Is there a natural remedy for me at //×? If I could only get there to check it out.

I need a plan.

Part 4

Leaving the Valley with a Plan

Chapter 25 – But I am 70

As I've previously conveyed, Valley Management will happily show me the way out if I give up on *PARALLEL* and sign on the dotted line accordingly. It's a devilish type of deal. Although I want out, I haven't seriously considered signing...yet. Quite the opposite. I am inspired.

But something daunting joins with that inspiration. I also feel like an unknotted, bursting at the seams, party balloon that has been let go. I enthusiastically zig and zag with my // ideas but know that without a re-fill soon, the balloon will sputter and drop lifeless. My ideas die again.

Today, I had a particularly discouraging and sobering thought that caused the Valley walls to suddenly close in. At this very moment, I am backed into a dark canyon. Everything is precipitous and feels impossible, impenetrable. There is no way out.

What discourages me is unrelated to climate change or, at first glance, seemingly so. It is my remembering of the 2012 Sandy Hook Elementary shooting in Newtown, Connecticut and the 2018 shooting at Marjory Stoneman Douglas High School in Parkland, Florida.

But it is related.

How much more precious than the slaughter of our children does it have to get to ban semi-automatic weapons or at least reasonably restrict their access? How many mothers and fathers, grandparents, aunts and uncles, and countless others have been ripped apart by this senseless carnage?

And in turn, how many gun control activists pace here with me in the Valley of Death, walking around in shock and disbelief that despite their loss, outrage, and advocacy, despite the fact that 56% -70% of Americans support a related ban, semi-automatic weapons persist, and the killing goes on and on (POLITIFACT, September 12, 2019)?

How much more precious than the upending of our planetary life support systems does it have to get before there is a full-scale mobilization to stop or slow down CO_2 build-up and global warming? How many coral reefs do we have to lose? How many tens of thousands of acres of the Amazon must be burned year after year? Why have large corporations prevailed and government policies failed even though a majority of Americans believe in human fueled climate change? And not just Americans. The majority of people around the globe (surveyed by Pew Research Center in 2018) from Brazil to South Korea to Kenya recognize our warming globe as a major threat.

And logically, why would I ever think that if the slaughter of our children doesn't move us to instant action on an assault weapon ban that something more abstract and complex to understand like the acidification of our oceans would result in the actions and changes needed, like shutting down CO_2 emissions on scale, to make a difference?

You see the parallel?

Of course, what I am alluding to here is the obvious impossible chasm to span that practical people point to every time I open my mouth. But this is why they will never have stories to regale others with, as I do, from the Valley of Death.

I am not sure if bragging rights are actually what I have or want.

The Truth of the Matter.

The snags and truths are this. I have been trying to drive myself towards the eye of the needle without having any idea where it is. There is no Valley management or rather I am Valley management. I can leave anytime I want. But my *PARALLEL* impulse cannot. And I do not seem to be able to leave it behind. So, I am stuck trying to figure out a way to exit the Valley with a resurrection idea. How can *PARALLEL* live?

But I am 70. That impossible chasm of time lies between me and finding a way. Is it possible to negotiate?

Yes, absolutely yes. But by me? I have my doubts, which leaves me grappling here as I am and perhaps also leaves you frustrated with me because I haven't got to the punchline.

Chapter 26 – The Punchline

When I started writing, I was mostly processing the disappointment of not advancing the // Bank and *Climate Emergency Credit Card* ideas. Since this past June 2020, in these COVID times, I've been here in the Valley faithfully sitting beside the carcass of my impulse. I am very loyal to *PARALLEL*, but not out of pride, guilt, or obligation. It is too young and too important to die. Otherwise, I would happily exit this place and breathe a sigh of relief.

Much to my surprise, I have kept on writing and what I refer to as a carcass is clearly not dead. *PARALLEL* has a lot more flesh on its bones than it did 10 months ago, but it is not animated. It is in a coma. Less medically, *PARALLEL* is a "sleeping beauty" waiting for its magic kiss. Who will the kisser(s) be? I seem to be hoping that it is the you and you and you and you....... somewhere out there.

I have finally realized that the only way to leave the Valley of Death with *PARALLEL* in tow and still asleep is to take it out on my back as a book. I didn't realize I was writing a book as an exit strategy until now. I thought I was writing a lament and processing my failure. I thought I was filling in the empty space left to me in the wake of these COVID-19 times. No holidays. No hugs. No travel. No swimming. Just writing, in the absence of everything else, some expression of my inner life's yearning and imagination.

Ordinarily, I would dismiss the notion of writing a book out-of-hand. The task is so daunting. I have done it once in 2010 – *The Earth's Best Story*, co-authored with my brother Arnie. But again? And to what end?

Now, fully vaccinated, and seeing the shadow of my COVID-life, albeit barely perceptible, in the rear-view mirror, I am waking up to the understanding that I didn't decide to write a book and then face the daunting-ness of it or not. I have just plodded along in a COVID-stupor, jotting down for months a hodgepodge of chronicles, reflections, inspirations and bemoanings and voila, as if it were me waking up from a deep sleep, there is a small book or almost one in front of me.

And this little book that I am, in this very moment, penciling in the title: *PARALLEL – A Climate Revolution Plan* – is my ticket out of the Valley.

A breakthrough of sorts for sure, the period to a two year long run-on sentence – the punchline that delivers my best shot at a plan to somehow incarnate *PARALLEL*.

But I am not celebrating. My best shot is a flimsy one.

I thought *The Earth's Best Story* was a well-written, instructive, and captivating tale that would reach hundreds of thousands of entrepreneurs, become a staple read for students in MBA programs, and find its way to some of the many parents who were loyal customers over the more than 30 years the company has been in business.

I was so wrong. Not, of course, about the well-written, instructive, and captivating tale part, but everything else. The publisher, Chelsea Green, printed 5000 books in 2010 and there has not been a second printing. I know it resides in many libraries. I know my best friend Amazon sells used copies.

But it is fair to say "case closed" on the size of the audience that found its way to *The Earth's Best Story*.

Why will – *PARALLEL* – be any different?

Three words come to mind.

Timing, Fate, and Marketing

Why not timing or readiness? In a May 2016 Inc. Magazine article by Chris Haroun, he writes:

Wayne Gretzky was the most successful hockey player in history. He was not successful because he skated to where the puck is. Rather, he skated to where the puck is going to be.

Maybe, *PARALLEL* represents where the puck is going to be. And if so, it will resonate. Chris Haroun continues:

The right idea at the right time is a major driver of success.... Yahoo's purchase of social media pioneer GeoCities for 3.6 billion in 1999 could have produced Facebook-like returns for investors.... Unfortunately, Yahoo was way too early.

And so, it goes. Big companies get it wrong all the time. Think Apple's Newton, Microsoft's early tablet strategy, or Oracle's failed Network Computer strategy. But these companies live to see another day.

Start-up failures are a dime a hundred dozen because of timing. Too early. Too late. They often don't live to see that other day. But what about timing that lands just right? That would be, in my estimation, *PARALLEL*.

Is there such a thing as fate or destiny? I think it is fair to say the question is debatable. Maybe fate reflects the expression of what we don't perceive: the unseen but present. It magically appears as if it were meant to be, but it actually already was.

Carbon dioxide, CO_2, is invisible until the temperature drops to around -109F. Then it is visible as dry ice. When the conditions are just right, from out of nowhere comes something that, without our 21st century understandings, would be incomprehensible. Nonetheless, CO_2 was always there with or without the understanding.

If fate exists, it is certainly not driven by morals or justice as fate should be (if I were the architect of the Big Show). So, I don't think *PARALLEL* is fated to be, but maybe it already IS.

So, from my altered state here in the Valley, I see the ducks lining up.

Duck #1 – The timing for *PARALLEL* is spot-on. Climate change awareness has caught on fire. The angst no longer lurks on the fringe, it has reached mainstream.

Duck #2 – *PARALLEL* already exists in, if you will, a parallel dimension. Why not? After all, how did I think of it? Hence, maybe // is fated to be if the two dimensions simply meet each other. More on that in a moment.

Duck #3 – The world is interconnected by the speed of light. Communication at scale is an everyday reality. Beyond memes and videos, what if climate change transformation went "viral?" What if the *Climate Emergency Credit Card* went viral? Why not? Technologically, at least, change or impact at scale is possible. Morally, practically, and factually we are in a crisis, and it is needed. So, how can it not be possible? Duck #3 says it is and I believe her.

How do two parallel dimensions meet? Serendipity? A science fiction novel?

Marketing?

I've Decided to Leave the Valley.

That's the big news. I have been ruminating here long enough.

I'm going to self-publish *PARALLEL,* and get it out there in every way I can. Call it marketing. Then, the wait begins. Will someone who also sees the parallel dimension I am glimpsing, respond? Could that someone responding be one of those individuals in the metaphorical room I wrote about earlier, one of the powerful, an influencer, moneyed and connected? Someone who sees it and gets it. Will it be the A-list: People like Bill McKibben, Paul Hawken, Greta Thunberg, Naomi Klein, Al Gore, John Kerry, Barack Obama, Gina McCarthy, Marilyn Waite, Oprah Winfrey, Bill Gates, Lady Gaga, Tom Steyer and the many others?

Unlikely, right?

The good news is that I have a back-up plan.

I'm going to package and pitch the // *Climate Emergency Credit Card.* Of course, it won't be for real for real. There is no // Bank or credit card yet. Nonetheless, I'm going to ask people who discover my campaign to sign a petition of sorts that declares that they are ready to sign up. They want the card. And they want the *PARALLEL* movement when it becomes for real for real.

I'll set a minimum threshold of positive responders; let's call it 5,000 signees. If I get that or more, I am going to venture out on a limb and reach out again to Woorim Hindan at Akash Social Enterprise and Lewis Draper at Next Gen Power. And of course, Bill McKibben.

Maybe they will be impressed. Maybe something will shift. Maybe the parallel dimension will reveal itself and I will move from outsider to insider.

I believe in *PARALLEL.* I know I am onto something. And because I am not looking for any kind of personal benefit, I am not burdened or distracted by perfectly normal, yet also preoccupying self-interests.

This is the Time.

The messaging throughout what has become *PARALLEL* is all about the possible impossible. And as such I naturally project a ra-ra and can-do spirit that I like to think is also grounded. Yet, even with the above sketch of a plan taking shape, I admit to feeling discouraged at the outset.

The sobering re-reckoning with the Sandy Hook and Marjory Stoneman Douglas High School tragedies took most of the stuffing out of me. But I am bouncing back.

I think part of the point of my Valley life has been learning to let go. I don't mean give up. I don't mean burying my head in the sand. But I do mean accepting that, as much as I want to be a consequential part of the climate change solution, I "probably" will not be.

It is natural for us to think defeatedly like this. The climate problems are so big and we (or at least me) feel so small. And so, we all get backed into the SO-SO – the same old – same old corner that whispers sweet nothings into our ears like "you are nothing, nothing." And also insists that there is no real "we" because how could there be. It's impossible. We are divided nationally, racially, religiously, culturally, economically and on and on into countless sub-groups.

But when the news reads something like "The Colorado River that irrigates farms, powers electric grids and provides drinking water to 40 million people is drying up," it's time to latch onto the word I used directly above and give it some new meaning. That word is "probably" as in.... I will probably not be a consequential part of the climate solution.

"Probably" does not mean no. It is synonymous with possibility and hope and antagonistic to outright defeatism. We need this outlook from you and me now. This is the time.

PARALLEL is possible and not as a gimmick or a splash of feel-good environmentalism. But it requires a leap of faith from feeling small, disempowered and inconsequential, feelings I have struggled with on this journey, to fulfilling our collective human potential as shapers and transformers of the future.

We clearly have a cause to unite us. Now what?

My answer is to create our *PARALLEL* lives.

It is Time to Make Friends with the Impossible.

Today, June 5, 2021, I have begun my walk out of the Valley. My year-long presence there as a crash site, one of many, is nothing to be ashamed about. It is also not a badge of honor. It simply reflects a life lived, a life of striving, a life of trials and errors, failures, and a life of hopefulness.

The Valley is not a vacation spot, but rather a place of fascinating people with endless stories that will make you laugh and cry.

I feel sentimental as I take this familiar walk.

I am not reminiscing about *Recovery Power Foods* or *Brio Ice Cream*, historical business carcasses of mine that are still smoldering in the Valley. Rather I am feeling in awe of what unites us and connects us to this miraculous blue marble we all are living on.

Somehow, too many of us have forgotten that we are each truly part of this miraculousness. We are cosmic. Our bones, our hemoglobin have their origins in star dust. We are starry miracles for sure. Sounds impossible, doesn't it? It is time to make friends with the impossible.

I don't know if we are the only miraculous life in the universe, but we are all certainly Earthlings.

To all Earthlings I say this. Life on planet Earth, the life that sustains us, the life that many enjoy, is in danger of inalterably changing. We have all gotten a taste this past COVID year of what it means for life as we know it to dramatically change. Imagine if there were no vaccines to bail us out, to return us to some approximation of normal. Imagine the ongoing disruption and the needed adaptations. What would the new normal look like?

There are No Vaccines for Climate Change.

What happens when the 7,000,000 acres of Central Valley ag land in California can longer be supported by the irrigation system that makes it all happen? What happens when we start running out of water because we've pumped out the aquifers and climate change reduces the capacity of the 60,000 square mile Central Valley watershed?

What happens?

Rest assured it can be nothing good, given that half of the fruits, vegetables and nuts grown in the United States are from that valley.

COVID has given us a taste of an unthinkable scale and scope of disruption. People have died alone as family members grieve from afar. Public funerals and memorial services all but disappeared in 2020 and now much of 2021. Hugs, kisses, and handshakes unsafe. Schools unsafe. Restaurants unsafe. Travel unsafe. Living as we knew it, unsafe.

It happened and continues still, but there appears to be light at the end of this COVID tunnel.

On the other hand, when the oceans rise because the Greenland ice sheet is melting irreversibly and at an unprecedented rate, there will be no light at the end of the low-lying Miami Beach and New Orleans's tunnels. Low lying Bangladesh may lose approximately 11% of its land affecting 15 million people by 2050 (ejfoundation. org/reports/climate-displacement-in-bangladesh).

Desertification caused by climate change and land mismanagement, such as over grazing and unsustainable freshwater use, threatens the food security of more than 2 billion people (Carbon Brief, August 6, 2019).

Rising CO_2 and methane levels, and in turn ocean temperatures, causes ocean acidification. As a result, many marine ecosystems hang in the balance.

The global warming tunnel, relative to our short human life spans is forever dark.

There is a disaster reel waiting in the wings for our children and grandchildren.

Is climate catastrophe still too much of an abstraction? Well, if COVID-19 has not been a wake-up call to not only the possibility of catastrophe but the experience of it, you probably are no longer reading this book.

<u>Again, Stupid is as Stupid Does.</u>

I understand that if *PARALLEL* ever sees the light of day, it will be politicized and demonized. For example, the New Confederates will jump all over my suggestion to increase the gasoline tax evoking a socialist take-over and engendering fear and resistance.

There will be Eeyore's, naysayers, and conspiracy theorists. Anything and everything will insist on obstructing. The SO-SO is a mighty force. It will fight for its life, but rest assured it will continue to be ambivalent to yours and mine.

I repeat there are no vaccines for climate change. There are no mulligans or do-overs. There is only significantly reducing fossil fuel consumption and CO_2 emissions and re-wilding as fast as furious as possible.

What stands in the way is this.

The scale of the climate crisis is global. We don't experience ocean acidification. It's an abstraction. We don't think much of a 1-degree F increase in average temperatures. It's nothing. Species extinction doesn't seem relevant to our everyday lives. We had a good winter of snow. Spring is normal. And on and on. The cautionary tale of the frog lulled into complacency as the water surrounding him gets warmer and warmer and then hotter and hotter to his end is, of course, just for stupid frogs, certainly not us.

Accompanying this incomprehensible scale and the mostly invisible and complex ecological impacts of a warming globe are our everyday human thought constructs. Labels like "alarmist," "doomsayer," and "Chicken Little – The Sky is Falling." In effect, if you can't see it, hear it, feel it, or smell it, it's not real. Hence, you have the presence of climate change deniers. This mind-set also stands in the way.

Two words capture the foundation of this dangerous human failing – ignorance and arrogance.

We witness a lot of this failing today, amplified by run-away social media platforms and amoral news organizations and compounded by a public education system with far too many deficiencies.

The only consolation I can offer is my belief that in the battle for hearts and minds, there are increasingly more people getting on board to accept the realities of climate change and the need to somehow respond to the crisis. Responding to the crisis in an effectual way has stood in the way of changing the disruptive arc of global warming.

And this brings me to summarizing the arc of my journey.

I started out being kind of like a regular widget environmentally conscious and concerned individual. A case could be made that I started out more advanced than that since I co-started the first organic baby food company in the United States. But I'm pushing back against that case because in the realm of climate change action, there is nothing special about me. Until recently, I owned a Prius. I have contributed as a small donor to Green Peace, VPIRG, and NRDC for many years. I angst. But I still fly for vacations. I don't have any solar panels. I burn oil and wood.

Then I read the open letter in the Guardian in April 2019 and became galvanized with alarm when I understood that those immersed in the climate field like Bill McKibben acknowledged that we were, as a species, going down the global warming drain. My response, naively or not, was disbelief and an obsession to do something.

Two years have passed, much of it in these COVID times and much of it spent psychologically in the Valley of Death licking my wounds and living into my imagination – reality be damned.

This has been my journey to *PARALLEL*.

Afterword

A 12-story condominium high rise collapsed in Surfside, Florida. More than a 150 people are still unaccounted for. First responders are still on the scene. Some families are grieving. Some are waiting, fearing the worst. Prayers are being offered from around the world. Calls for unity amidst the shared crisis and loss abound. Cries to get to the bottom of this catastrophe are saturating the public air and media spaces. Outrage is being expressed. Lawyers are filing suits.

Structural engineers are analyzing video of the collapse. A 2018 engineering report of the structure has surfaced pointing to *"abundant cracking and spalling"* of concrete columns, beams and walls in the parking garage. The same firm detailed in an earlier report that the ground floor pool deck of the building was resting on a concrete slab that *"had major structural damage."* (New York Times, June 26, 2021)

Repairs back in 2018 were estimated to be more than $9.1 million (Floridian News Times, June 27, 2021). And the repair work had not yet been done.

What does this calamity have to do with climate change or *PARALLEL?*

Although it is still early days (at the time of this July 2021 writing) to definitively attribute the cause of this collapse, there were significant warnings and concerns that were ignored.

Perhaps some residents knew of the engineering report or even read it. Many, no doubt, saw the cracking and deterioration of the concrete in the parking garage, maybe even on a daily basis. The pool area problems were also probably obvious. The threatening news of the significant cost of the repairs probably spread through the condominium complex like wildfire, even if the details did not. And the engineering science was not controversial. The damage was real.

Do you see the parallel?

The building in the minds of those living in it and/or responsible for it was too big to fail. It was their "world" and it felt big. You could count on it. It had stood for 40 years. How could it just, in an instant, pancake into a heap of rubble and lost lives?

And yet those same minds were also surrounded by information and empirical evidence that arguably should have galvanized immediate action. The foundation their lives was built on was literally crumbling. They were warned, not of the imminent collapse, but of major structural damage. There was evidence plain to see. Yet, everything still "felt" normal enough. The elevators worked. The building was not a leaning tower. People were not scared to death. The dots that were obvious (crumbling concrete pillars) did not connect to the dots that were not. And a reality too big to fail, failed.

Climate scientists have been sounding the global warming alarm for decades now. Our planetary life support systems are a reality far more complex and invisible than the failing concrete support pillars of that 12-story building. Earth failure is not only inconceivable, but also incomprehensible because we don't see ocean currents, much less understand them. We don't see CO_2. Most of us do not attribute the shrinking reservoirs of Lake Mead, Lake Powell and Trinity Lake to the shaky "12-story building" under attack in South America called the Amazon Rainforest.

This May (2021), the average global level of atmospheric CO_2 rose to 415 parts per million (ppm). The last time CO_2 levels were so elevated was 3 million years ago when sea levels were 50 feet higher and we, so called modern humans, did not exist (Time, May 14, 2019).

It was 113F in Portland, Oregon on June 28, 2021. One data point, a daily temperature reading, usually means nothing, if in fact it was only one data point. But 113F is an aberrant data point within a sea of aberrant data points spread across the globe.

Most of us are not paying attention. We may be inconvenienced and decide to buy an air conditioner. That's about it. Many of us care, but don't know what to do. Some are more engaged within a wide spectrum of activism. But so far, our lives and lifestyles are going on and will go on, just as the lives in that Surfside condo did until about a week ago when the unimaginable happened.

The condo association received its alarming engineering report. We, citizens of the planet, have been receiving dire reports and alarming global warming trends for decades. The condo residents saw the deterioration, just as we see or learn of unprecedented sea-level rise, decimated coral reefs, rising global temperatures, and disappearing glaciers.

The condominium residents had to face the cost of repair and did not in a timely way, just as we collectively are confronted with the costs of our fossil fuel addiction and the loss of mangroves and peat bogs and their natural carbon sequestering capabilities. And yet we are also not responding in a timely way with the necessary actions and adaptations.

You see where this may be headed. Hence, my dedication at the beginning of this book.

To the many millions across the globe who are resilient in their hope and determination to meet the global warming crisis.

To the many who will answer the call and come together to form a movement, a mighty bucket brigade of small and large actions that add up to a transformation of how we live and consume on our Earth.

To the "impossible" which may be a door to new horizons and not just a ceiling that declares the limitations of our human potential.

AND

To the many millions who will be displaced, the many who will die, suffer, and live lives without the stability and security of the Earth's planetary life support systems.

To the species that will become extinct because of climate change.

And to all the future prayers, tears, and trauma needlessly spoken, shed, and felt.... if.... we humans choose to react to tragedy rather than act to prevent it.

PARALELL is presented as a path to prevent the predictable and inevitable losses that are coming if we do not act. Why not unite in solidarity in advance of the "building" collapse rather than unite afterwards in shared grief and bewilderment? Why not find our way to new horizons?

What I see is that the possible is failing us. That failing is just what tragically happened in Surfside, Florida. And that faltering is why our Earth is warming as it is and why our planetary life support systems are imperiled.

I have done my best to imagine an impossible that would not fail us.

To // or not to //, that is the question. Not a question or choice for all of us, but certainly for many who live in representative democracies and who have a certain degree of economic security. What amazing good fortune it is to have such power and choice in life. This good fortune also carries a responsibility. It does not last forever. The "building" – "our building" – is not too big to fail, but I believe it is also not doomed to fail.

That is my hope and the reason I am putting this message of possibility, now a little book with a big plan, into a bottle in a rising sea and sending it out into the world.

Acknowledgements

I want to first thank Bill McKibben. My recognition, by happenstance, of his name amongst 22 other notable activists in an April 3, 2019 letter to *The Guardian* newspaper declaring that there is not the urgency needed to prevent our planetary life-support systems from spiraling into collapse launched my journey to *PARALLEL*.

My brother Arnie Koss has been by my side on the development of *PARALLEL* from the beginning. He has encouraged and challenged me with the best spirit imaginable. The book in your hands or on your tablet is a tribute to his efforts to help bring *PARALLEL* to life.

Brother-in-law Peter Claghorn was my second reader. He brought to me new perspectives on my writing style and a boat load of suggested edits that have proved to be invaluable. And he challenged me to deepen some of my research and to be more aware of how, at times, I was being unnecessarily polarizing despite my intention to be otherwise.

Sister-in-law Melly Flynn is a copy editor extraordinaire. Her corrections and suggestions were a revelation to me. *PARALLEL* is a much better read thanks to her. Wherever this book falls short, there is a good chance I did not heed her advice.

The skepticism and resistance that my sons, Gabe and Aaron, maintained throughout my writing effort pushed me to understand them and to keep trying to make // relevant. I can't say that I succeeded in winning them over, but I do know their candor energized me to try to see *PARALLEL* through their eyes and created a determination to anticipate their criticisms and answer the questions I imagined that would keep them forever on the sidelines and apart from *PARALLEL*. A father can hope.

My good friends David Fried and Jonni Corcoran reminded me to stay true to myself amidst the flurry of re-write and re-structuring ideas that regularly came my way. Their support and connection to me helped me to trust some of my deeply felt impulses and not to abandon them.

Carley Claghorn, my dear wife, has ridden with me side by side throughout my entire entrepreneurial life. And she has always been supportive. A true testimony to her nervous system, her belief in me, and her generous spirit. She has watched the development of *PARALLEL* from afar not knowing what to make of it. As this book has taken shape, she has weighed in expressing encouragement and concerns. I have learned to pay close attention to these moments despite my natural defenses. She is usually right and *PARALLEL* is now closer to the book I want it to be thanks to her wise counsel.

Lastly, I want to acknowledge the real people I interfaced with known here only by their pseudonyms – Woorim Hindan, Josh Allen, Lewis Draper, and Peter Neal. These individuals engaged with me wholeheartedly and did everything they could to support my raw ideas and imaginations. No matter the Valley of Death outcome, I appreciate their patient efforts to engage with me and value their dedication to being difference-makers in a world that needs difference-makers more than ever.

Addendum A
The Climate Emergency Credit Card

"Two existential crises are developing with terrifying speed, climate breakdown and ecological breakdown; neither is being addressed with the urgency needed to prevent our life support systems from spiraling into collapse."

— April 3, 2019 letter to *The Guardian Newspaper* signed by 23 of the world's leading climate activists including Bill McKibben, Greta Thunberg, and Naomi Klein.

The Stage is Set
The threat of climate catastrophe is upon us. Traditional forms of activism are failing. Relatively few belong to environmental organizations. Millions are sitting on the sidelines as disempowered spectators, struggling with inaction, isolated from each other across the globe, and feeling resigned.

There are plenty of "moments" of sporadic activism like *Strike for the Climate* and *Extinction Rebellion*. Climate awareness is growing. Greta Thunberg is a household name. But there is no everyday 24-7 global climate "movement." There is nothing unifying and empowering for the majority sitting on the sidelines to trust, believe in and make a connection. And it is exactly this everyday connection that is needed to unleash the human potential that might prevent our life support systems from spiraling into collapse.

We need a movement.

Introducing the Climate Emergency Credit Card
This is a big idea. Big ideas are the only ones that can really tackle the climate crisis.

Consumption is arguably the root of ecological decline. It is counter-intuitive to suggest a credit card as the point of a climate-activism spear. But the end of consumption is not a feasible solution to the climate emergency. The question then is, how do we make the *"buying of things,"* which everyone does, work for re-wilding the planet and de-carbonizing our everyday lives?

The answer is the Climate Emergency Credit Card, the first global card that is dedicated 100% to fighting climate change.

The possibility of having a big part of our everyday mundane life, that is the *"buying of things,"* become a part of the fight for the climate is a powerful prospect. Multiply that possibility by tens of millions of cardholders and you have, ready to harness, a vast amount of untapped human potential (and capital).

Add to that potential the focus of bringing more understanding/ consciousness to the impact of the *"buying of things"* by showcasing (via the *climate emergency card.org* website) new information and perspectives that result in better choices for the planet and we've taken an important step forward.

Every time the *Climate Emergency Card* is used, and it is a strikingly beautiful green card, it makes a statement. It stands for a hopeful future. You know every possible dollar is being funneled to credible and well-vetted efforts to meet the climate change crisis. It offers and reinforces every day meaning and connection to the greater good.

The First Climate Emergency Bank
To create this Credit Card dedicated 100% to fighting climate change, we also need a not-for-profit bank standing behind it, also 100% dedicated. Imagine *The First Climate Emergency Bank.* This virtual (no bricks and mortar) initiative provides a means to be independent of the for-profit demands of commercial banks that by definition must direct most of their profits to stockholders.

Together and for the first time, the Climate Emergency Bank and Card will create a vehicle for anyone and everyone to become instantaneously connected and unified as an "activist" community fighting for the climate.

Instead of serving its stockholders as most banks must do and placating its cardholders with frequent flyer miles and cash back rewards as most credit cards do, the Climate Emergency Bank and Card exclusively serve ecological restoration and de-carbonizing, serve our planet and every critter on it, and serve our children and theirs into the future.

Not for Profit
This means that, after covering administrative expenses, all proceeds from interest, card processing fees, membership fees, and investments will be directed to funding critical environmental efforts.

Also importantly, the aim of the *First Climate Emergency Bank* and the CLEM card is not to reinvent the wheel and become another environmental organization, with all the associated overhead, competing for members and scarce funding dollars. Quite the opposite.

The aim is rather to mobilize engagement, catalyze action, inspire community, and be an ally and collaborator everywhere possible for climate activism including being a potential funder for projects initiated by established groups like *Green Peace, 350.org, Sierra Club* and *World Wildlife.*

A Means to Create the "Urgency Needed"

There are many "feel good" credit cards offered by established organizations like the *World Wildlife Fund (WWF)*, *Sierra Club*, and *Green Peace.* These Affinity Card Programs, as they are commonly called, are sponsored by the largest for-profits banks. The WWF Card, for example, from Bank of America authorizes the payment of 0.08% of net retail purchases to the organization. WWF receives $800 for every million dollars of purchases. Also received by WWF is $3.00 for each card subscriber and annual card renewal.

These contributory schemes, although well meaning, are constrained by commercial banking realities. They do not represent the "urgency needed" to prevent our life support systems from spiraling into collapse.

Conversely, the Climate Emergency Bank and Credit Card will create a dedicated platform to specifically express that urgency needed. In doing so, it will capture billions of consumer dollars and re-direct them towards the fight for the planet and for future generations.

These dollars will represent a burgeoning climate activist movement, united at first by merely a shared green credit card held in millions of wallets, but ultimately united by the experience of shared empowerment as each cardholder begins to experience the impact upon the world that their everyday ordinary lives is a part of.

Economic Accessibility

The ethos of the *Climate Emergency Card* is to be accessible to as many people as possible. The actual program details to do this will be fleshed out in a creative business plan development process. But conceptually and for illustration purposes, it is easy to imagine a card committed to:

- Low annual membership fees at the discretion of the cardholder: $0 — $40 — $80 — $120
- Low interest intro rates for new card holders
- Below market ongoing APR rates
- Online-only bank presence resulting in lower operating costs than traditional brick and mortar banks.

Environmental Expertise
A world class team of environmental scientists and activists will advise the *Climate Emergency Card* program. These experts will be responsible for guiding the profits derived from the card's activity to the most impactful projects that champion de-carbonizing and ecological restoration.

Transparency
The bank and credit card operations will be built upon a platform of 100% transparency. Members can engage directly with the organizations they are supporting. CLEM will gather news and provide project updates creating a live feed of climate change news. This will help deepen the sense of participating in a movement and could even develop into something akin to a TV Channel dedicated to climate/environmental news, networking and activism. There is a world of possibility to explore here.

Founding Leadership Advisory Group
A *Founding Leadership Advisory Group* needs to form to set the momentum to develop a comprehensive *Climate Emergency Credit Card* business plan. This founding group represents wisdom, capacity, resilience, know-how, and entrepreneurial spirit.

A hands-on team of banking, regulatory, capital planning, cybersecurity, organizational development, social and digital media, public relations, marketing, and entrepreneurial expertise will be formed around the plan which will then serve as the primary selling document to capitalize the start-up.

An *International Scientific Advisory Board* will also be built by leveraging the prominence and engagement of the Founding Leadership Group. This Board will inform key decisions as to what projects to financially support and promote to maximize the impact of the organization.

Summary
A climate emergency is upon us. It threatens the life support systems we all depend on and the future for all generations. The global scale and the related complexities imposing themselves are, if not incomprehensible, then seemingly insurmountable.

Most people are not engaged with the problem. Many are cynical and resigned. Others are concerned but can think to do little more than recycle and be as environmentally responsible as practical. Some have a more "activist" outlook and provide membership support to organizations like Green Peace and NRDC.

There is plenty of talk and more and more action, but there is no cohesive movement. The urgency needed to meet the crisis is lacking according to the world's leading climate activists. What can be done?

Imagine with us the *First Climate Emergency Bank* and Credit Card. It needs to happen.

Made in the USA
Middletown, DE
17 December 2021

54102816R00102